Algebra

Robert Taggart

D1262420

WALCH PUBLISHING

POWER BASICS ®

Senior Author	Robert Taggart
Editorial Director	Susan Blair
Project Manager	Kate O'Halloran
Project Editor	Erica Varney
Director of Marketing	Jeff Taplin
Senior Production Editor	Maggie Jones
Interior Design	Mark Sayer
Cover Design	Roman Laszok
Typesetting	Sheila Russell
	Mark Sayer
	Ian Weidner
Editorial Staff	Gina Hamilton
	Elizabeth Lynch
	Richard Lynch
	Holly Moirs
	Mary Rich

1   2   3   4   5   6   7   8   9   10

ISBN 0-8251-5671-8

Copyright © 1997, 2000, 2005

J. Weston Walch, Publisher

P. O. Box 658 • Portland, Maine 04104-0658

walch.com

Printed in the United States of America

WALCH PUBLISHING

Table of Contents

To the Student

Welcome to *Power Basics® Algebra*. This book will help you learn how to solve basic algebraic equations and inequalities. Each lesson builds on what you have already learned. As you go through the lessons step by step, you will master basic algebra. This knowledge will help you at school, at work, and in other parts of your life.

In **Unit 1, Algebra Basics,** you will learn about negative numbers. You will learn how to add, subtract, multiply, and divide them. You will also learn how to combine terms and solve simple equations.

In **Unit 2, Solving Equations and Inequalities,** you will learn how to work with algebraic terms. You will add, subtract, multiply, divide, and simplify terms. You will also learn about inequalities and how to simplify and solve problems using inequalities.

In **Unit 3, Graphing Linear Equations,** you will learn two ways to graph the equations for lines on the coordinate plane. You will also learn how to find the slope of a line.

In **Unit 4, Polynomial Operations,** you will learn about three different types of algebraic expressions: monomials, binomials, and trinomials. You will also learn how to factor different types of algebraic expressions.

In **Unit 5, Quadratic Equations,** you will learn two ways to solve quadratic equations. You will also learn how to use the quadratic formula to solve word problems.

To the Student, *continued*

Each lesson is made up of short sections that explain important algebra concepts. Each of these sections is followed by a few problems to help you practice what you have learned. Each unit ends with a Unit Review. The Unit Review is followed by Application activities. These activities will let you extend and apply what you have learned in the unit.

Power Basics® Algebra has many special features that make learning easier. "Tips" give you hints on ways to master the ideas and facts in the text. "In Real Life" sections show you how the skills you are learning are used in the world outside the classroom. "Think About It" questions ask you to look at algebra in new ways. The "Words to Know" section at the start of most lessons includes important new terms introduced in the lesson. The first time each word is used, it is defined for you. This first use appears in **bold type.** All the terms in the "Words to Know" section are also defined in the Glossary at the end of the book. If you can't remember what a term means, you can look it up in the Glossary. Finally, the "Review of Rules and Formulas" at the back of the book includes the rules and other important information introduced in the book.

As you move through *Power Basics® Algebra*, you will become a more confident and skilled mathematician. We hope that you enjoy this material as you learn.

UNIT 1

Algebra Basics

LESSON 1: Negative and Positive Numbers

GOAL: To Identify negative and positive numbers

WORDS TO KNOW

absolute value	negative number	signed number
actual value	positive number	

What Are Negative and Positive Numbers?

We often think of numbers in positive terms. We say we have
2 dogs, or $10. But if you had no money and owed $20, how
would you say what you had? You would need to use numbers in
negative terms. You would say you had $–20. The –20 is a
negative number. Negative numbers are numbers with a value
of less than zero. They are the opposite of **positive numbers.**

Look at the number line below.

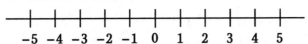

$$-5 \quad -4 \quad -3 \quad -2 \quad -1 \quad 0 \quad 1 \quad 2 \quad 3 \quad 4 \quad 5$$

Notice that the numbers on the left of zero have a minus sign (–)
in front. Numbers to the left of zero are called negative
numbers. Numbers to the right of zero are called positive
numbers. The number zero is neutral. It is neither negative nor
positive.

Now look at the number line below. This line has no numbers.
Put zero (0) in the center. Then write numbers to the right and left.

Does your number line look like the one at the top of the page?

Notice that the negative numbers always have a minus sign (–) in front. But now look at the positive numbers. The positive numbers have no sign in front. You can write positive numbers with or without a plus sign (+) in front. Look at the example below.

$$-5 \quad -4 \quad -3 \quad -2 \quad -1 \quad 0 \quad +1 \quad +2 \quad +3 \quad +4 \quad +5$$

The numbers +4 and 4 are the same. They are both positive. Whenever you see a number with no sign in front, it will always be positive.

We can refer to positive and negative numbers as **signed numbers.** The plus sign and minus sign show whether they are positive or negative.

THINK ABOUT IT

Why do you think positive numbers can be written with or without a plus sign in front, but negative numbers must always have a minus sign in front? Which kind of number do you use more often? Write your answer on a separate sheet of paper.

■ PRACTICE 1: What Are Negative and Positive Numbers?

Circle the correct answer for each question.

1. Look at the number line below. Is the circled number positive or negative?

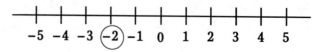

$$-5 \quad -4 \quad -3 \quad \boxed{-2} \quad -1 \quad 0 \quad 1 \quad 2 \quad 3 \quad 4 \quad 5$$

    a. positive   **b.** negative

2. Look at the number line below. Is the circled number positive or negative?

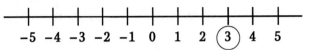

    a. positive   **b.** negative

3. Look at this number:

    +3

Is this number positive or negative?

    a. positive   **b.** negative

4. Look at this number:

    4

Is this number positive or negative?

    a. positive   **b.** negative

5. Look at this number:

    −4

Is this number positive or negative?

    a. positive   **b.** negative

6. Look at this number:

5

Which number below is the same as this number?

a. +5   **b.** −5

Larger and Smaller Numbers

Now you know that the numbers to the right of 0 are positive numbers. The numbers to the left of 0 are negative numbers. But how can you tell if one number is larger than another number?

Numbers to the right on a number line are always larger than numbers to the left.

Look at the circled numbers on the number line below.

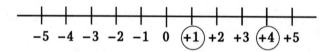

+1 is to the left of +4 on the number line. This means that +1 is smaller than +4. +4 is to the right of +1 on the number line. This means that +4 is larger than +1.

Look at the circled numbers on the number line below.

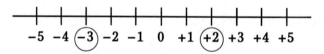

In the number line above, −3 is to the left of +2. This means that −3 is smaller than +2. +2 is to the right of −3. This means that +2 is larger than −3.

On a number line, all of the negative numbers are to the left of 0. This means that all negative numbers are smaller than 0. All of the positive numbers on a number line are to the right of 0. This means that all positive numbers are larger than 0.

TIP

It is important to remember that negative numbers must always have a minus sign (–) in front. This is easy to remember! You already know that positive numbers do not always have a sign. Think of all the numbers you see every day on receipts, price tags, menus, and so forth. These are all positive numbers. These numbers usually do not have a sign. Since you know that positive numbers do not always have a sign, you can guess that negative numbers must have a sign. If they didn't, we wouldn't be able to tell them apart from positive numbers!

■ PRACTICE 2: Larger and Smaller Numbers

Circle the correct answer for each question.

1. Look at the number line below. Which of the circled numbers is larger?

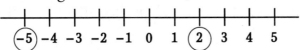

   a. 2   **b.** –5

2. Look at the number line below. Which of the circled numbers is smaller?

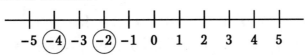

   a. –2   **b.** –4

3. Look at the number line below. Which of the circled numbers is larger?

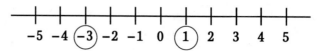

a. 1   b. −3

4. Look at the numbers below. Which number is smaller?
   a. 0   b. −1

5. Look at the numbers below. Which number is larger?
   a. −2   b. −5

6. Look at the numbers below. Which number is larger?
   a. 2   b. −2

Actual Values and Absolute Values

You have learned that numbers to the right on a number line are larger than numbers to the left. This is called the **actual value** of a number—what the number is really worth. The actual value of 3 is greater than the actual value of −2. The actual value of 4 is greater than the actual value of −4. When you talk about actual values, it is important to know whether a number is positive or negative. Positive numbers always have a greater actual value than negative numbers.

If you ignore (don't look at) the sign in front of a number and only think about how far it is from 0, then you are thinking about the number's absolute value. The **absolute value** of a number tells you how far it is from 0 on a number line. It tells you the value of the number without its sign. Look at the number line below.

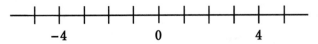

The number 4 is 4 units to the right of 0. The number –4 is 4 units to the left of 0. Both numbers are 4 units away from 0. The absolute value of 4 is 4. The absolute value of –4 is also 4.

Remember that each negative number is the exact opposite of a positive number. They are both exactly the same distance from zero. The absolute value of a number will stay the same whether the number is positive or negative.

For example, look at the numbers 7 and –7. The number 7 is to the right of –7 on a number line. The actual value of 7 is larger than –7. But both 7 and –7 are 7 units away from 0 on a number line. This means that 7 and –7 have the same absolute value: 7.

The absolute value of –7 is 7. The absolute value of –5 is 5. Notice that the actual value of –5 is greater than the actual value of –7. But the absolute value of –5 (5) is less than the absolute value of –7 (7).

■ PRACTICE 3: Actual Values and Absolute Values

Circle the correct answer for each question.

1. What is the actual value of –5?
    a. 5   **b.** –5

2. What is the absolute value of –5?
    a. 5   **b.** –5

3. What is the absolute value of 3?

    a. 3   **b.** −3

4. What is the absolute value of −3?

    a. 3   **b.** −3

Look at each pair of numbers below. Circle the number in each pair that has a larger actual value.

5. −5, +7   **6.** −9, +2   **7.** +8, −3

8. 3, −8   **9.** −7, −2   **10.** 2, +5

11. −1, −3   **12.** +6, 4

Look at each pair of numbers below. Circle the number in each pair that has a larger absolute value.

13. −5, +7   **14.** −9, +2   **15.** +8, −3

16. −7, −2   **17.** 2, +5   **18.** −1, −3

TIP

There is a special symbol for absolute value. The symbol looks like this: |3|. This means "the absolute value of 3." If you wanted to write "the absolute value of 5 equals 5," you would write:

$$|5| = 5$$

If you wanted to write "the absolute value of −25 equals 25," you would write:

$$|-25| = 25$$

LESSON 2: Operations with Signed Numbers

GOAL: To learn how to add, subtract, multiply, and divide positive and negative numbers

WORDS TO KNOW

subtrahend   **sum**

Adding Positive and Negative Numbers

You can use a number line to add numbers. Let's add two positive numbers using a number line.

Example 1

$$2 + 5 = ?$$

Step 1. Find the first number (2) on the number line below.

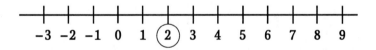

Step 2. The second number is 5. This is a positive number. Using the number line above, count 5 units to the right of 2. You move to the right because it is a positive number.

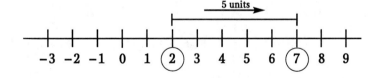

Step 3. You should now be on the number 7.

$$2 + 5 = 7$$

Example 2

Now we will try another example. Let's add −3 and 2.

Step 1. Find the first number (−3) on the number line below.

$$-3 + 2 = ?$$

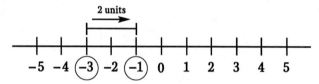

Step 2. The second number is 2. This is a positive number, so you move to the right. Start at −3 and count 2 units to the right.

2 units

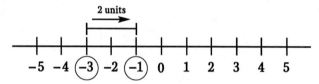

Step 3. You should now be on the number −1.

$$-3 + 2 = -1$$

Remember, when the second number is positive, count to the right of the first number.

So what do you do when the second number is negative? Let's try an example.

Example 3

Let's add 6 and −5.

Step 1. Find the first number (6) on the number line below.

$$6 + (-5) = ?$$

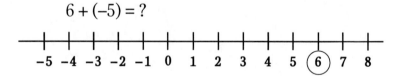

Step 2. Now look at the second number: –5. This is a negative number. Negative numbers are the opposite of positive numbers, so you go in the opposite direction. When the second number is a negative number, count to the left of the first number. You move to the left because it is a negative number.

How many units do you move? To find out, take the absolute value of the second number. In this example, the second number is –5. The absolute value of –5 is 5. So, starting at 6, move 5 units to the left.

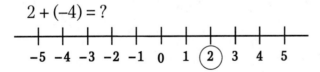

Step 3. You should now be on the number 1.

$$6 + (-5) = 1$$

Example 4

Let's try one more example: $2 + (-4)$.

Step 1. Find the first number (2) on the number line below.

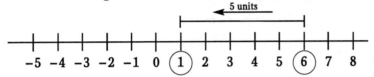

Step 2. Now look at the second number: –4. This is a negative number, so you should move to the left. The absolute value of $-4 = 4$, so move 4 units to the left.

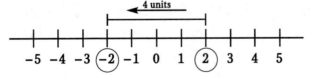

Step 3. You should now be on the number –2.

$$2 + (-4) = -2$$

TIP

To add numbers on a number line, look at the second number. If it is positive, move to the right. If it is negative, move to the left.

■ PRACTICE 4: Adding Positive and Negative Numbers

Use the number line to solve each problem below. Write your answer on the line after each problem.

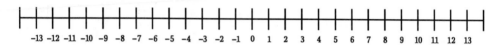

1. $2 + 5 = $ _____

2. $12 + (-7) = $ _____

3. $-6 + 7 = $ _____

4. $-1 + (-2) = $ _____

5. $0 + 4 = $ _____

6. $0 + (-6) = $ _____

7. $-3 + (-2) = $ _____

8. $4 + (-8) = $ _____

The First Rule for Addition

You have learned how to add positive and negative numbers on a number line. Now you will learn how to add them without a number line.

Look at the examples below.

Example 1 $(+5) + (+7) = +12$

Example 2 $(-5) + (-7) = -12$

Look at example 1 above. All the numbers in example 1 have the same sign (positive). Now look at example 2 above. The numbers in example 2 also have the same sign (negative).

In example 1, both of the numbers being added are positive. The **sum**—the result of adding—is also positive.

In example 2, both of the numbers being added are negative. The sum is also negative.

The numbers in example 1 have the same absolute values as the numbers in example 2.

- The absolute value of both +5 and −5 is 5.
- The absolute value of both +7 and −7 is 7.
- The absolute value of both +12 and −12 is 12.

You have just learned the first rule for adding signed numbers:

First Rule for Addition

When you add signed numbers that have the same sign, add the absolute values and keep the same sign.

Let's look at a few examples.

Example 3

$$(+4) + (+5) = ?$$

Step 1. First, look at the signs of the numbers to be added. In this example, they both have the same sign (positive). This tells you that you can use the first rule of addition to add them.

Step 2. Find the absolute values of both numbers. The absolute value of +4 is 4. The absolute value of +5 is 5.

Step 3. Add the absolute values.

$$4 + 5 = 9$$

Step 4. Look at the signs on the numbers you added. The numbers you added were both positive. This tells you that the answer should also be positive.

$$(+4) + (+5) = +9$$

Example 4

$$(-2) + (-3) = ?$$

Step 1. First, look at the signs of the numbers to be added. In this example, the two numbers being added have the same sign (negative). This tells you that you can use the first rule of addition to add them.

Step 2. Find the absolute values of both numbers. The absolute value of –2 is 2. The absolute value of –3 is 3.

Step 3. Add the absolute values.

$$2 + 3 = 5$$

Step 4. Look at the signs on the numbers you added. The numbers you added were both negative. This tells you that the answer should also be negative.

$$(-2) + (-3) = -5$$

IN REAL LIFE

Think of the money you owe as a negative number. Each time you get a bill, change the amount you owe to a negative number. Keep track of your bills by adding the negative numbers together. For example, Ana receives a phone bill for $30.00 (–30) and an electric bill for $22.00 (–22). She adds the bills together: $-30 + (-22) = -52$. Now Ana knows that she owes $52.00.

■ PRACTICE 5: The First Rule for Addition

Use the first rule for addition to solve each problem below. Write each answer on the line.

1. $(+9) + (+2) = $ _____

2. $(-8) + (-3) = $ _____

3. $(-6) + (-4) = $ _____

4. $7 + 3 = $ _____

5. $(-8) + (-7) = $ _____

6. $(-3) + (-2) = $ _____

7. $(-32) + (-27) = $ _____

8. $(+43) + (+31) = $ _____

9. $9 + 39 = $ _____

10. $(-12) + (-52) = $ _____

11. $(-98) + (-13) = $ _____

12. $25 + 75 = $ _____

The Second Rule for Addition

You have learned that when you add two numbers with the same sign, your answer will also have that sign. Now you will learn a rule for numbers that don't have the same sign.

Here is the second rule for adding signed numbers.

Second Rule for Addition

When you add signed numbers that have different signs, subtract the smaller absolute value from the larger absolute value. Then use the sign of the number with the larger absolute value.

Look at the two examples below.

Example 1

$$(+6) + (-4) = ?$$

Step 1. First, look at the signs on the numbers to see which rule you should use. In this example, the two numbers being added have different signs. This means that you should use the second rule for addition to add them. This rule tells you to first subtract the smaller absolute value from the larger absolute value.

Step 2. Find the absolute value of each number.

The absolute value of +6 is 6. The absolute value of −4 is 4.

Step 3. Subtract the smaller absolute value from the larger absolute value. 4 is smaller than 6, so subtract 4 from 6.

$$6 - 4 = 2$$

Step 4. The rule also tells you that your answer should have the sign of the number with the larger absolute value. You already know that 6 is the larger absolute value. 6 is the absolute value of +6. +6 has a positive sign, so the answer should be positive.

$$(+6) + (-4) = +2$$

Example 2

$$(+2) + (-7) = ?$$

Step 1. First, look at the signs on the numbers to see which rule you should use. In this example, the two numbers being added have different signs. This means that you should use the second rule for addition to add them. The rule tells you to subtract the smaller absolute value from the larger absolute value.

Step 2. Find the absolute value of each number.

> The absolute value of +2 is 2. The absolute value of –7 is 7.

Step 3. Subtract the smaller absolute value from the larger absolute value. Subtract 2 from 7.

> $7 - 2 = 5$

Step 4. You know that 7 is the larger absolute value. 7 is the absolute value of –7. –7 has a negative sign, so the answer should be negative.

> $(+2) + (-7) = -5$

THINK ABOUT IT

Death Valley is 282 feet below sea level (sea level = 0). If you are in Death Valley and you see a tree that is 60 feet high, how far below sea level is the top of the tree? Write your answer on a separate sheet of paper.

■ PRACTICE 6: The Second Rule for Addition

Use the second rule for addition to solve each problem below. Write each answer on the line.

1. $(+12) + (-5) = $ _____ **2.** $(-4) + (+2) = $ _____

3. $(-11) + (+3) = $ _____ **4.** $(+8) + (-9) = $ _____

5. $(+9) + (-11) = $ _____ **6.** $(-3) + (+8) = $ _____

7. $(+3) + (-8) = $ _____ **8.** $(-45) + (+90) = $ _____

9. $(+37) + (-29) = $ _____ **10.** $(+96) + (-70) = $ _____

11. $-93 + 84 = $ _____ **12.** $-46 + (+46) = $ _____

13. $92 + (-53) = $ _____ **14.** $15 + (-53) = $ _____

15. $(-35) + 76 = $ _____ **16.** $(-10) + 54 = $ _____

Subtracting Positive and Negative Numbers

You have already learned how to add signed numbers. Now you will learn how to subtract signed numbers.

There is only one rule for subtracting signed numbers.

> **Rule for Subtracting Signed Numbers**
>
> When you subtract signed numbers:
>
> 1. Change the sign of the second number.
> 2. Add the two numbers. (Be sure to use the correct addition rule.)

Look at the two examples that follow.

Example 1

$$(+8) - (+3) = ?$$

Step 1. Check the signs of both numbers. In this example, both numbers are positive.

Step 2. The rule for subtracting signed numbers tells you to change the sign of the second number (+3).

$$(+8) - (-3) = ?$$

Step 3. The next step tells you to add the two numbers.

$$(+8) + (-3) = ?$$

Notice that the two numbers you need to add now have different signs, so you should use the second rule of addition to add them. Subtract the smaller absolute value from the larger absolute value. The absolute value of +8 is 8. The absolute value of −3 is 3. 8 is larger than 3, so you should subtract 3 from 8.

$$8 - 3 = 5$$

Step 4. The second rule of addition also tells you that the answer should have the same sign as the number with the largest absolute value. You already know that 8 is the larger absolute value. 8 is the absolute value of +8, which is positive. So the answer should also be positive.

$$(+8) - (+3) = +5$$

Example 2

$$(+8) - (-3) = ?$$

Step 1. Check the signs of both numbers. This example asks you to subtract a negative number from a positive number.

Step 2. The rule for subtraction tells you to change the sign of the second number (−3).

$$(+8) - (+3) = ?$$

Step 3. The next step of the rule tells you to add the two new numbers, +8 and +3. Both numbers have the same sign, so use the first rule of addition to add them. Add the absolute values of the two numbers and keep the same sign. The absolute value of +8 is 8. The absolute value of +3 is 3. 8 + 3 = 11.

$$(+8) - (-3) = +11$$

TIP

The second number in a subtraction problem is called the **subtrahend.** When you follow the first step of the rule for subtraction, be sure you only change the sign of the subtrahend.

■ PRACTICE 7: Subtracting Positive and Negative Numbers

Use the subtraction rule to solve each problem below. Write each answer on the line.

1. $+5 - (+3) =$ _____

2. $-5 - (-3) =$ _____

3. $+5 - (-3) =$ _____

4. $+3 - (+5) =$ _____

5. $-3 - (-5) =$ _____

6. $+3 - (-5) =$ _____

7. $-3 - (+5) =$ _____

8. $-5 - (-5) =$ _____

9. $-68 - (+27) =$ _____

10. $+49 - (+32) =$ _____

11. $+25 - (-13) =$ _____

12. $-7 - (+98) =$ _____

Multiplying and Dividing Signed Numbers

You now know how to add and subtract positive and negative numbers. In this lesson, you will learn how to multiply and divide positive and negative numbers.

Look at the examples below. Can you see a pattern?

$$(+6) \times (+2) = +12 \qquad\qquad (+6) \times (-2) = -12$$

$$(+6) \div (+2) = +3 \qquad\qquad (+6) \div (-2) = -3$$

$$(-6) \times (-2) = +12 \qquad\qquad (-6) \times (+2) = -12$$

$$(-6) \div (-2) = +3 \qquad\qquad (-6) \div (+2) = -3$$

If the two numbers being multiplied or divided have the same sign, the answer is always positive. If the numbers being multiplied or divided have different signs, the answer is always negative.

These are the rules for multiplying and dividing signed numbers.

Rule 1: Multiplying or Dividing Numbers with the Same Sign

    If the signs of both numbers being multiplied or divided are the same, the answer will be positive.

Rule 2: Multiplying or Dividing Numbers with Different Signs

    If the signs of the numbers being multiplied or divided are different, the answer will be negative.

Look at the examples that follow.

Example 1

$$6 \times (-3) = ?$$

In this example, the numbers being multiplied have different signs. Review rule 2. You will see that the answer will be a negative number.

$$6 \times (-3) = -18$$

Example 2

$$(-6) \times (-3) = ?$$

In this example, the numbers being multiplied have the same sign (negative). Review rule 1. You will see that the answer should be a positive number.

$$(-6) \times (-3) = +18$$

Example 3

$$(+21) \div (+7) = ?$$

In this example, the numbers being divided have the same sign (positive). Review rule 1. The answer should be a positive number.

$$(+21) \div (+7) = +3$$

Example 4

$$(+21) \div (-7) = ?$$

In this example, the numbers being divided have different signs. Review rule 2. The answer should be a negative number.

$$(+21) \div (-7) = -3$$

■ PRACTICE 8: Multiplying and Dividing Signed Numbers

Solve each problem below. Write your answer on the line after each problem.

1. $-4 \times 5 = $ _____

2. $12 \div 2 = $ _____

3. $-8 \times (-1) = $ _____

4. $6 \times (-2) = $ _____

5. $5 \times (-3) = $ _____

6. $-9 \div 3 = $ _____

7. $9 \times (-2) = $ _____

8. $-45 \div 9 = $ _____

9. $24 \div 6 = $ _____

10. $(-18) \div (-9) = $ _____

LESSON 3: Algebra Concepts

 GOAL: To understand and use basic algebra terms and concepts

WORDS TO KNOW

algebraic expression	divisor	solve
coefficient	expression	term
combining like terms	like terms	unknown number
dividend	parentheses	variable

Basic Terms and Symbols

In Lesson 2, you learned how to add, subtract, multiply, and divide signed numbers. Now you will learn to use these skills to solve problems in algebra.

Algebra is often used to find the value of a number you don't know. This is called an **unknown number.** Letters of the alphabet are used to stand for unknown numbers. These letters are called **variables.** Their value can vary from problem to problem.

Look at this problem:

$$3 + ? = 7$$

This problem asks you to find an unknown number—the number you can add to 3 to get 7. You can use a variable—x—to write the problem:

$$3 + x = 7$$

The letter x stands for the number you are trying to find.

To work with variables, we need to learn some new symbols.

- When you multiply, do not use an "×" in algebra problems. This could be confused with a letter used as a variable. Instead, put **parentheses**—( )—around the second number.

> **To Show Multiplication**
> $5 \times 8 = 40 \longrightarrow 5(8) = 40$

- If you want to multiply a number and a variable, do not use an "×" or parentheses. Just write the variable next to the number. 5 times x is written as $5x$. Always write the number first, before the variable. This number is called the **coefficient** of the variable.

> **To Multiply a Number and a Variable**
> $5 \text{ times } x \longrightarrow 5x$

- Use a line to show division. The number being divided—the **dividend**—goes above the line. The number you are dividing by—the **divisor**—goes below.

> **To Show Division**
> $10 \div 5 = 2 \longrightarrow \dfrac{10}{5} = 2$

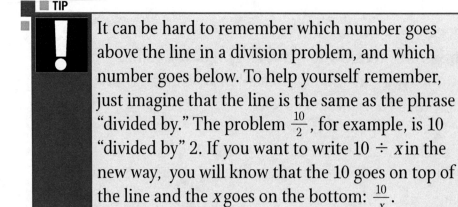

TIP

It can be hard to remember which number goes above the line in a division problem, and which number goes below. To help yourself remember, just imagine that the line is the same as the phrase "divided by." The problem $\frac{10}{2}$, for example, is 10 "divided by" 2. If you want to write $10 \div x$ in the new way, you will know that the 10 goes on top of the line and the x goes on the bottom: $\frac{10}{x}$.

■ PRACTICE 9: Basic Terms and Symbols

Rewrite each problem below using the new symbol. Write your answer on the line after each problem.

Example: 5 times 3 = 5(3)

1. 4 times 9 = _____   **2.** 8 times 12 = _____

3. 6 times 5 = _____   **4.** 3 times 3 = _____

Rewrite each problem below. Write your answer on the line after each problem.

Example: 8 times $z = 8z$

5. y times 19 = _____   **6.** x times 3 = _____

7. 9 times f = _____   **8.** 8 times m = _____

Rewrite each problem using the new symbol. Write your answer on the line after each problem.

Example: $16 \div 4 = \dfrac{16}{4}$

9. $x \div 12 =$ _____   **10.** $24 \div y =$ _____

11. $5 \div 2 =$ _____   **12.** $z \div 18 =$ _____

13. $y \div 3 =$ _____   **14.** $m \div 10 =$ _____

Solving Terms

A **term** is a number or a variable, or a combination of both. Terms can stand alone or they can be with other numbers.

These are all examples of terms:

$$c \qquad \frac{b}{2} \qquad 7 \qquad \frac{14x}{x} \qquad 12z$$

If you know the value of a variable, you can find out the value of a term. This is called **solving** a term.

Look at the two examples below.

Example 1

$$\text{If } m = 4, \text{ then } 3m = ?$$

In this example, you know that $m = 4$. Because you know what m is (4), you can solve the term $3m = ?$ To do this, write the number 4 in place of the letter m:

$$3m = ? \qquad\qquad 3(4) = ? \qquad\qquad 3(4) = 12$$

Since m is 4 and $3(4) = 12$, then $3m = 12$.

Example 2

$$\text{If } y = 6, \text{ then } \frac{y}{2} = ?$$

In this example, you know that $y = 6$. To solve the term, write the number 6 in place of the letter y:

$$\frac{y}{2} = ? \qquad\qquad \frac{6}{2} = ? \qquad\qquad \frac{6}{2} = 3$$

Since y is 6 and $\frac{6}{2} = 3$, then $\frac{y}{2} = 3$.

■ PRACTICE 10: Solving Terms

Solve each term below. Write your answer on the line after each term.

1. If $b = 5$, then $14b =$ _____
2. If $k = 7$, then $\dfrac{21}{k} =$ _____
3. If $m = 17$, then $2m =$ _____
4. If $q = 9$, then $3q =$ _____

Solving Expressions

One meaning for the word **expression** is "a way of saying things." An **algebraic expression** is a way of saying things with numbers and variables. Algebraic expressions are made up of terms with operation signs between them.

These are all algebraic expressions:

$$5 + 7 \qquad x - 9 \qquad \frac{3a}{2} + 7 \qquad \frac{3a}{2}$$

You have just learned how to solve algebraic terms. You can also solve algebraic expressions. Look at the examples below.

Example 1

$\qquad$ If $k = 5$, then what is the value of $(k + 1)$?

In the example above, you know that $k = 5$. Because you know the value of k, you can solve this expression. To do this, write the number 5 in place of the letter k:

$$k + 1 = ?$$
$$5 + 1 = ?$$
$$5 + 1 = 6$$

The answer is $k + 1$ is equal to 6.

Example 2

If $n = -2$, then what is the value of $(7 + n)$?

In this example, you know that $n = -2$. Solve the expression by writing the number -2 in place of the letter n:

$$7 + n = ?$$
$$7 + (-2) = ?$$
$$7 + (-2) = 5$$

The answer is $7 + n$ is equal to 5.

Example 3

If $m = 5$, then what is the value of $(2m - 3) + 3m$?

In this example, you know that $m = 5$. Solve the expression by writing the number 5 in place of the letter m:

$$(2m - 3) + 3m$$

$$(2(5) - 3) + 3(5)$$

$$(10 - 3) + 15$$

$$7 + 15 = 22$$

The answer is $(2m - 3) + 3m$ is equal to 22.

■ PRACTICE 11: Solving Expressions

Solve each expression that follows. Write your answer on the line after each expression.

Example: If x is 12, then $4x - 3$ is equal to 45.
$$4(12) - 3 = ?$$
$$48 - 3 = ?$$
$$48 - 3 = 45$$

1. If $b = 5$, then $27 - 3b$ is equal to _____.

2. If $m = 9$, then $\dfrac{27}{m} + 2$ is equal to _____.

3. If $n = 7$, then $3n - 5 + 2n$ is equal to _____.

4. If $s = 4$, then $s + \dfrac{s}{2} + 3s$ is equal to _____.

Combining Like Terms

You already know that a variable stands for an unknown number. Here's a way to help you understand variables. Suppose you had several boxes filled with books. Some boxes are labeled "x." These boxes all have the same number of books in them. Other boxes are labeled "y." Each "y" box has the same number of books as every other "y" box. You do not know how many books are in the "x" boxes or the "y" boxes.

Example 1

Suppose you have 2 "y" boxes, 3 "x" boxes, and 3 loose books. You want to find out the total number of books.

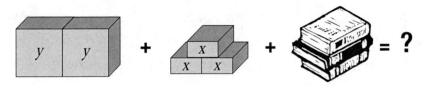

You could use x and y to stand for the number of books in each box, and say: $2y$ books + $3x$ books + 3 books = ? Even simpler, you could leave out the word "books" and just write $2y + 3x + 3 = ?$ This means $2y$ (the number of books in 2 "y" boxes) + $3x$ (the number of books in 3 "x" boxes) + 3 (3 loose books).

Your friend Malia has 4 "y" boxes and 8 loose books.

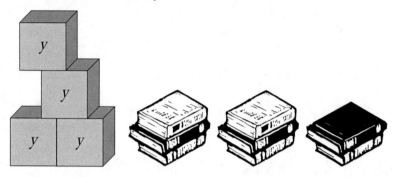

You could write Malia's books as $4y + 8$. This means $4y$ (the number of books in 4 "y" boxes) + 8 (8 loose books).

Suppose you wanted to add your books and Malia's books. Then the boxes would look like this:

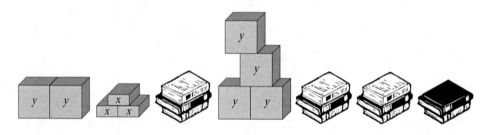

You could write this as: $2y + 3x + 3 + 4y + 8$. But this would be a strange way to stack books and boxes. You'd probably put all the things that were like one another together. You'd put all the y boxes together, all the x boxes together, and all the loose books together:

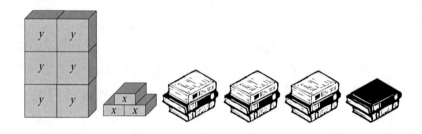

You can do the same with the expression $2y + 3x + 3 + 4y + 8$. This expression is very long and confusing! You can make this expression shorter by combining the numbers that describe the same things. Start with the 3 and the 8. They both describe the same thing—known numbers. Combine them by adding them together: $3 + 8 = 11$.

$$2y + 3x + 4y + 11$$

You can also combine the y's. Because all the y's have the same value, they describe the same thing. To combine them, add the coefficients—the numbers that multiply the variables: $2y + 4y = 6y$.

$$6y + 3x + 11$$

Numbers with the same variable are called **like terms.** When you make an expression shorter by adding or subtracting numbers with the same variable, you are **combining like terms.** Remember, you can only combine numbers with the same variable. In the expression $6y + 3x + 11$, you can't combine $6y + 3x$. This is as short as this expression can be.

When you combine like terms, pay special attention to the sign before each term. Look at the example below.

Example 2

$$3x + 5 + 2x$$

You can combine the x's to make this expression shorter. Remember to bring their signs with each term:

$$3x + (+2x) + 5 = 5x + 5$$

Here is another example.

Example 3

$$3x + 5 - 2x$$

Again, you can combine the x's. Pay attention to the sign before each term.

$$3x + (-2x) + 5 = x + 5$$

Review your rules for addition to help you work correctly!

Now look at one more example.

Example 4

$$3x - x + 2 + 7b + 2x - 5b$$

Can you make this expression shorter? There is only one number that does not have a variable (2). You cannot combine this number with any other number. But there are three terms that have x's. Combine the x terms:

$$3x - x + 2x = 4x$$

$$4x + 2 + 7b - 5b$$

Now you can combine the b terms.

$$7b - 5b = 2b$$

$$4x + 2 + 2b$$

You have combined all the like terms in this expression.

Suppose you are going on a picnic. You have to tell your friend how much fruit you can bring. First, you look in your refrigerator. You see 3 oranges, 1 banana, and 2 apples. Then you look in your pantry. In your pantry, there are 2 oranges, 4 bananas, and 5 apples. Would you tell your friend that you have 3 oranges, 1 banana, and 2 apples in your refrigerator, and 2 oranges, 4 bananas, and 5 apples in your pantry? No, you would probably add each kind of fruit together. You would say "I can bring 5 oranges, 5 bananas, and 7 apples." You have just combined like terms!

■ PRACTICE 12: Combining Like Terms

Combine the like terms in each expression below. Write each answer on the line.

Example: $3m + 2m = 5m$

1. $5x + 7 - 6 = $ _____

2. $9y - 2y + 3y = $ _____

3. $4z + 9 - 2 - z = $ _____

4. $3c + 9y + 3c + 7 = $ _____

5. $2m + 5 + 6m - 7 = $ _____

6. $5n + \dfrac{2}{x} - 3n - 6 = $ _____

7. $7y - 6y = $ _____

8. $14z - 9 - 13z + 5 = $ _____

9. $-4 + 17g + 2 - 27g = $ _____

10. $3b - 9 + 18 - 7b = $ _____

LESSON 4: Algebraic Equations

 GOAL: To learn how to combine like terms, perform inverse operations, and check your work

WORDS TO KNOW

equation   **inverse operation**   **solution**

Algebraic Equations

So far, you have learned some special words used in algebra and special ways of writing algebraic expressions. Now you will learn about equations.

An **equation** is a mathematical statement. It says that one quantity (one or more numbers) is equal to another quantity. An equation always contains an equal sign.

You have been writing equations for years. Look at some examples.

$$2 + 5 = 7 \qquad\qquad x - 9 = 2$$

$$(3)(15) = 45 \qquad\qquad 3b = 45$$

$$\frac{75}{5} = 15 \qquad\qquad \frac{b}{3} = 25$$

As you can see, equations can have both numbers and variables.

An equation tells you that two mathematical quantities are equal. An equation has two sides. There is an equal sign in the middle. Look at the equation below. Notice that the left side $(24 + 6)$ is equal to the right side (30).

$$24 + 6 = 30$$

If you add the same number to both sides of an equation, both sides will still be equal.

$$(24 + 6) + 5 = 30 + 5$$

$$35 = 35$$

If you subtract the same number from both sides of an equation, both sides will still be equal.

$$(24 + 6) - 5 = 30 - 5$$

$$25 = 25$$

If you multiply both sides of an equation by the same number, both sides will still be equal.

$$(24 + 6)(5) = 30(5)$$

$$150 = 150$$

If you divide both sides of an equation by the same number, both sides will still be equal.

$$\frac{24 + 6}{5} = \frac{30}{5}$$

$$6 = 6$$

As long as you do the same thing to both sides of an equation, the sides will remain equal.

There are just two main rules for solving algebra problems. Here is rule 1.

Rule 1 for Solving Algebra Problems

You can do anything to an equation as long as you do exactly the same thing to *both* sides of the equation.

The word "equation" means "making equal." To show that both parts of an equation are equal, an equal sign (=) is always used. So if it doesn't have an equal sign (=), it isn't an equation.

An equation is like a scale. The equal sign is in the middle. If you do something to one side of the scale, you must do the same thing to the other side so the scale will stay balanced. Look at the example below.

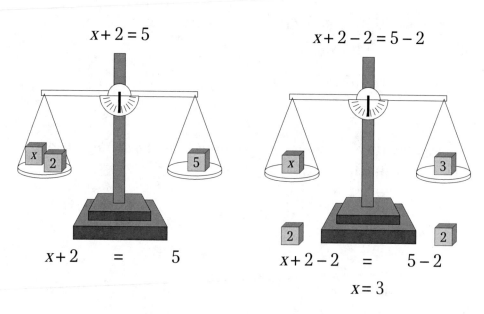

$$x + 2 = 5$$

$$x + 2 - 2 = 5 - 2$$

$$x + 2 \quad = \quad 5$$

$$x + 2 - 2 \quad = \quad 5 - 2$$

$$x = 3$$

If you do the same thing on both sides, the scale stays balanced. If you just changed one side, the sides wouldn't balance. They would not be equal.

■ THINK ABOUT IT

Is $3y + y$ an equation? Why or why not? Write your answer on a separate sheet of paper.

Equations with Variables

In algebra, equations often have variables. Variables are letters that stand for unknown numbers. Look at the example below.

$$x + 5 = 17$$

In this equation, x is a variable. Its value is unknown. How can you find its value? You have already learned rule 1 for solving algebra problems. Here is rule 2.

Rule 2 for Solving Algebra Problems

To find the value of an unknown

Step 1. Combine any like terms, *and*

Step 2. Do the opposite of what has been done to the variable to both sides of the equation.

What does this rule mean? Well, you already know how to do the first part—combine like terms. But what does the second part of the rule mean?

Let's look at the following examples.

Example 1

$$x + 5 = 17$$

Step 1. Look at step 1 of rule 2. Can you combine any like terms in this equation? No, you cannot combine x and 5. They are not like terms.

Step 2. Now let's try step 2 of rule 2. The equation asks you to add 5 to the variable x. What is the opposite of adding 5? It is subtracting 5. So, to find the value of x, subtract

5 from both sides of the equation. Remember, you must always do the same thing to both sides of an algebraic equation.

$$x + 5 - 5 = 17 - 5$$

Step 3. Now, try to combine like terms again to get your answer. You can combine 5 and –5 (5 – 5 = 0), and 17 and –5 (17 – 5 = 12).

$$x + 0 = 12$$
$$x = 12$$

When you substitute 12 for x, the equation is true.

$$x + 5 = 17$$
$$12 + 5 = 17$$

The **solution** to this equation—the value for x that makes the equation true—is 12.

Example 2

$$x - 3 = 7$$

Step 1. First, try to combine any like terms. There are no like terms in this equation.

Step 2. Next, notice that the number 3 is being subtracted from the variable (x). You want to find the value of x. What is the opposite of subtracting 3? It is adding 3. This means that you must add 3 to both sides of the equation to find the value of x.

$$x - 3 + 3 = 7 + 3$$
$$x = 10$$

Example 3

$$3x = 21$$

Step 1. First, try to combine terms. There are no like terms in this equation.

Step 2. Next, try to find the value of the variable (x). In this equation, the variable (x) is multiplied by 3. What is the opposite of multiplying by 3? It is dividing by 3. To find the value of x, divide both sides of the equation by 3.

$$\frac{3x}{3} = \frac{21}{3}$$

$$\frac{\cancel{3}^1 x}{\cancel{3}_1} = \frac{x}{1} = x \qquad \frac{21}{3} = 7$$

$$x = 7$$

Example 4

$$\frac{x}{2} = 30$$

Step 1. First, try to combine like terms. There are no like terms in this equation.

Step 2. Next, find the value of the variable (x). In this equation, the variable (x) is being divided by 2. What is the opposite of dividing by 2? It is multiplying by 2. Multiply both sides of the equation by 2.

$$2\left(\frac{x}{2}\right) = 2(30)$$

$$\frac{2}{1}\left(\frac{x}{2}\right) = \frac{2x}{2} \qquad 60$$

$$\frac{\cancel{2}^1 x}{\cancel{2}_1} = \frac{x}{1} = x$$

$$x = 60$$

■ PRACTICE 13: Algebraic Equations

Solve each equation below. Write your answer on the line after each equation. Remember to ask yourself: (1) What has been done to the variable? (2) What should you do to both sides of the equation?

Example: $7a = 42$

$$\frac{7a}{7} = \frac{42}{7}$$

$$a = 6$$

1. $y + 9 = 12$ $y = \underline{\hspace{2cm}}$
2. $x + 17 = 42$ $x = \underline{\hspace{2cm}}$
3. $12z = 36$ $z = \underline{\hspace{2cm}}$
4. $s - 15 = 43$ $s = \underline{\hspace{2cm}}$
5. $29 + x = 35$ $x = \underline{\hspace{2cm}}$
6. $\dfrac{x}{6} = 7$ $x = \underline{\hspace{2cm}}$

Checking Your Work

Algebra problems are very easy to check. All you have to do is go back to the original equation. Then, put your answer in place of the variable.

Look at the example below.

Example 1

$$8x = 72$$

Step 1. To solve for x, divide both sides by 8:

$$\frac{8x}{8} = \frac{72}{8}$$

$$x = 9$$

Step 2. To check your answer, go back to the original equation. Put your answer (9) in place of the variable (*x*). Does the equation work? Are both sides equal?

$$8x = 72$$

$$8(9) = 72$$

$$72 = 72$$

Yes, your answer is correct!

It is always a good idea to check your work. Learning algebra is a step-by-step process. You need to check each step before you take the next one.

 IN REAL LIFE

 It is always important to check your math. This is true if you are doing math at work, balancing your checkbook, paying bills, or doing any other math. Mistakes can cost you money. If you make a mistake with your bank account, you might have to pay special fees. If you make mistakes at work, you could even lose your job! Always check your math carefully.

■ PRACTICE 14: Checking Your Work

Solve each equation that follows. Write your final answer on the line after each equation. Check your work.

Example: $9y = 36$ $y = 4$ checking the answer:

$$\frac{9y}{9} = \frac{36}{9}$$ $9(4) = 36$

$$y = 4$$ $36 = 36$

1. $\dfrac{b}{5} = 9$ $b =$ _____

2. $14c = 84$ $c =$ _____

3. $d - 25 = 75$ $d =$ _____

4. $g + 4 = 10$ $g =$ _____

5. $\dfrac{r}{6} = 7$ $r =$ _____

6. $7t = 35$ $t =$ _____

Inverse Operations

You just learned rule 2 for algebraic equations. You learned to look at an equation, notice what had been done to the variable, and do the opposite to both sides of the equation. Another word for "opposite" is "inverse." Doing the opposite of what was already done is called an **inverse operation.**

Look at the two examples that follow.

Example 1

$$3y + 9y - 2y = 100$$

Step 1. Remember the steps of rule 2. First, try to combine like terms. You can combine the y's: $3y + 9y - 2y = 10y$.

$$10y = 100$$

Step 2. Next, try to find the value of y. What has been done to the variable (y) in this equation? You can see that y is being multiplied by 10. This means that you must divide both sides of the equation by 10 to find the answer. This is the inverse operation.

$$\frac{10y}{10} = \frac{100}{10}$$
$$y = 10$$

Example 2

$$5m + m = 40 + 2$$

Step 1. First, try to combine any like terms. You can combine the m's: $5m + m = 6m$. You can also combine the numbers without variables: $40 + 2 = 42$.

$$6m = 42$$

Step 2. Next, find the value of m. What has been done to the variable (m)? In this equation, m has been multiplied by 6. This means you must divide both sides by 6 to find the answer. This is the inverse operation.

$$\frac{6m}{6} = \frac{42}{6}$$
$$m = 7$$

■ PRACTICE 15: Inverse Operations

For each equation below, notice what has been done to the variable. Then say what the inverse operation is for each one. Write your answer on the line beside each equation.

Example: $5x = 20$ Inverse operation: <u>divide both sides by 5</u>

1. $5y = 45$ Inverse operation: _____

2. $\dfrac{a}{7} = 3$ Inverse operation: _____

3. $x + 3x = 12$ Inverse operation: _____

4. $12b - 2b = 50$ Inverse operation: _____

Sometimes you will need to solve a word problem in algebra. For example: What is 10% of 20? Remember that the word "what" always stands for the number you do not know yet (a variable). The word "is" always stands for an equal sign (=). The word "of" always stands for a multiplication sign. Now change each word to its correct symbol: $x = 10\%(20)$. This means "What is 10% of 20?" Now all you have to do is change the percent to a fraction or decimal and multiply!

$$x = 10\%(20)$$

$$x = \frac{10}{100}\left(\frac{20}{1}\right) \quad\quad \text{OR}$$

$$x = \frac{200}{100}$$

$$x = 2$$

$$x = 10\%(20)$$

$$x = .10(20)$$

$$x = 2$$

2 is 10% of 20.

Solving for Variables

In some equations, you will see variables and numbers on the same side of the equal sign. Look at the example below.

$$4x = 10 + 2x$$

In order to solve an equation like this, all the variables must be moved to one side of the equal sign. All the numbers without variables must be on the other side of the equal sign. Your goal is to have the variable alone on one side. How can you do this? Look at the example below.

Example 1

$$4x = 10 + 2x$$

Step 1. In this example, you must move $2x$ to the other side. This way all the variables ($4x$ and $2x$) will be on one side. All the numbers without a variable (10) will be on the other side. How do you move $2x$ to the other side? Notice that the $2x$ is being added to the 10. To get rid of the $2x$, you must do the inverse operation: Subtract $2x$ from both sides. Then combine like terms.

$$4x - 2x = 10 + 2x - 2x$$

$$2x = 10 + 0$$

$$2x = 10$$

Step 2. Now, to find the value for x, you must get rid of the 2. This will leave the x by itself. You can see that the x is being multiplied by 2. Do the inverse operation: Divide both sides by 2. Then combine any like terms.

$$\frac{2x}{2} = \frac{10}{2}$$

$$x = 5$$

Step 3. Check your answer.

$$4x = 10 + 2x$$

$$4(5) = 10 + 2(5)$$

$$20 = 10 + 10$$

$$20 = 20$$

Now look at another example.

Example 2

$$5y - 10 = 40$$

Step 1. In this example, there are numbers without variables on both sides of the equation. You want to move 10 over to the side with the 40. How can you do this? Notice that the 10 is being subtracted from the left side. Do the inverse operation: Add 10 to both sides. Then combine like terms.

$$5y - 10 + 10 = 40 + 10$$

$$5y = 50$$

Step 2. Now you want to move the 5 away from the y. This will leave the y alone. Notice that the 5 is being multiplied by y. Do the inverse operation: Divide both sides by 5. Then combine like terms.

$$\frac{5y}{5} = \frac{50}{5}$$

$$y = 10$$

Step 3. Check your answer.

$$5y - 10 = 40$$

$$5(10) - 10 = 40$$

$$50 - 10 = 40$$

$$40 = 40$$

■ PRACTICE 16: Solving for Variables

Solve each equation below. Write each answer on the line. Check all your answers carefully.

Example: $8c = 4c + 24$ $c = 6$

$\qquad\quad 8c - 4c = 4c - 4c + 24$ $8(6) = 4(6) + 24$

$\qquad\quad \dfrac{4c}{4} = \dfrac{24}{4}$ $48 = 24 + 24$

$\qquad\quad c = 6$ $48 = 48$

1. $5b = 2b + 21$ $b =$ _____

2. $2y - 8 = 12$ $y =$ _____

3. $3x - 1 = x + 9$ $x =$ _____

4. $3m + 5 = 14$ $m =$ _____

UNIT 1 REVIEW

Circle the correct answer for each question or problem below.

1. Look at the number line below. Which of the circled numbers is larger?

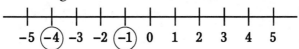

    a. -1 **b.** -4

2. Look at the numbers below. Which number has a larger absolute value?

    a. -3 **b.** $+5$

3. $-20 + 15 = ?$

    a. -5 **b.** 15

    c. 35 **d.** 5

4. $40 - (+15) = ?$

    a. 55 **b.** 60

    c. -15 **d.** 25

5. $-30 \times (-5) = ?$

    a. 6 **b.** 150

    c. -150 **d.** -25

6. $-65 \div 5 = ?$

    a. 325 **b.** -70

    c. -13 **d.** 15

7. If $x = 4$, then $\dfrac{12}{x} = ?$

    a. 16 **b.** 48 **c.** 3

8. Combine like terms in this expression: $y - 2x + 8 + 2y$.

    a. $4y + 2x - 8$ **b.** $3y - 2x + 8$ **c.** $y - 2x + 8$

9. Look at the equation: $\dfrac{x}{20} = 2$. What is the value of x?

    a. 20 **b.** 2

    c. 40 **d.** 10

10. Look at the equation: $2x + 6 = 4x + 2$. What is the value of x?

    a. 2 **b.** 1

    c. 3 **d.** 4

UNIT 1 APPLICATION ACTIVITY 1
People in Math

Many people have added to our knowledge of mathematics. Some early mathematicians include Diophantus, al-Khwārizmī, Carl Friedrich Gauss, George Boole, Évariste Galois, and Sir Isaac Newton. Research one of these mathematicians. Or choose some other mathematician who interests you. To do the research, you can use the library, interview a math teacher, or search the Internet.

- Whom did you study?

_____

- When and where did this person live?

_____

- Write a paragraph below about why this person was important to the study of algebra.

_____

_____

_____

_____

_____

_____

UNIT 1 APPLICATION ACTIVITY 2
Patriotic Percentages

In this activity, you will practice changing word problems to algebraic equations. First, find an encyclopedia and an atlas of the United States. Use the atlas, encyclopedia, and the algebra skills you learned in Unit 1 to answer the questions that follow on the next page.

Let's try one question as an example.

- What percentage of today's United States were the original 13 colonies?

First, change this question into an algebraic equation. *What percentage* is the number you want to find. This is your variable (x). The 13 colonies were our first "states." In today's United States, there are 50 states. So you want to find what percent of 50 is 13. Remember that the word *of* stands for a multiplication sign. The word *is* stands for an equal sign. So you can write the equation as $x\%(50) = 13$. Now use your algebra skills to solve the equation:

$$x\,(50) = 13$$

$$50x = 13$$

$$\frac{50x}{50} = \frac{13}{50}$$

$$x = \frac{13}{50}$$

Use a calculator to find that 13 divided by 50 equals 0.26, which equals 26%. The original 13 colonies were 26% of today's 50 states.

Now go ahead and try the questions below. Remember, use your atlas and/or encyclopedia to find the information. Then change the question into an equation, and solve!

- What percentage of the states in the United States start with the letter *N*?

  Equation: _____ Answer: _____%

- What percentage of the states in the United States were added after 1900?

  Equation: _____ Answer: _____%

- What percentage of the United States is your state?

  _____%

- What percentage of the states in the United States are west of the Mississippi River?

  Equation: _____ Answer: _____%

UNIT 2

Solving Equations and Inequalities

LESSON 5: Solving Equations

GOAL: To learn how to simplify and solve equations and equations with squared variables

WORDS TO KNOW

constant	exponent	square root
cubed	formula	squared
denominator	numerator	squared variable
distance formula	reciprocal	

Solving Equations by Subtracting and Adding

When you solve an equation, you want to get the variable by itself. This way, you can find the value of the variable. Look at the equation below.

Example 1

$$x + 6 = 13$$

In this equation, you want to get the x by itself. To do this, you must get rid of the 6. Notice that 6 is being added to x. To get rid of the 6, do the opposite operation: Subtract 6. This is called doing the inverse operation. The word *inverse* means "opposite." If you subtract 6 from the left side, you must subtract 6 from the right side, too. Then both sides of the equation remain the same.

$$x + 6 - 6 = 13 - 6$$

$$x = 7$$

By subtracting the same number from both sides of the equation, you get x by itself: $x = 7$. The solution is 7.

Example 2

Try another equation: $m - 30 = 67$. In this equation, you want to get rid of the 30 so the m will be by itself. Notice that 30 is being subtracted from m. Do the inverse operation: Add 30. Do this to both sides of the equation.

$$m - 30 + 30 = 67 + 30$$

$$m = 97$$

TIP

When you solve for a variable, you can check to see if your answer is correct. Just put your answer in place of the variable in the original equation. Then see if the equation still works. Look at the example below.

$$x + 2 = 7$$

$$x + 2 - 2 = 7 - 2$$

$$x = 5$$

Now check your answer.

$$x + 2 = 7$$

$$5 + 2 = 7$$

$$7 = 7$$

Yes, your answer is correct!

■ PRACTICE 17: Solving Equations by Subtracting and Adding

Solve each equation below. Write your answer on the line after each equation.

1. $x + 3 = 24$ $x =$ _____

2. $z + 450 = 2467$ $z =$ _____

3. $h - .5 = 4$ $h =$ _____

4. $z - 36 = 683$ $z =$ _____

5. $q - 70 = 120$ $q =$ _____

6. $m - 12 = 45$ $m =$ _____

Solving Equations by Dividing and Multiplying

Equations can also be solved by using division and multiplication.

Example 1

Look at the following equation.

$$9x = 27$$

In the equation above, you must get rid of the 9 to get the x by itself.

Notice that 9 is being multiplied by x. To get rid of 9, do the inverse operation: Divide by 9. Do this to both sides of the equation.

$$\frac{9x}{9} = \frac{27}{9}$$

$$x = 3$$

You now know that you must get a variable by itself to find its value and solve an equation. You have learned that when a number is added to a variable in an equation, you must subtract that number from both sides of the equation. When a number is subtracted from a variable, you must add that number to both sides of the equation. When a variable is multiplied by a number in an equation, you must divide both sides by that number. Lastly, when a variable is divided by a number in an equation, you must multiply both sides by that number.

Look at the example below.

Example 2

$$\frac{x}{3} = 9$$

To get the x by itself, you must multiply both sides of the equation by 3.

$$\frac{3}{1}\left(\frac{x}{3}\right) = 3(9)$$

$$\frac{3x}{3} = 27$$

$$x = 27$$

■ PRACTICE 18: Solving Equations by Dividing and Multiplying

Solve each equation on the next page. Write your answer on the line after each equation.

Example: $6z = 24$

$$\frac{6z}{6} = \frac{24}{6}$$

$$z = 4$$

1. $10x = 150$　　　　　　　$x =$ _____

2. $84 = 3m$　　　　　　　$m =$ _____

3. $\dfrac{n}{4} = 12$　　　　　　　$n =$ _____

4. $\dfrac{f}{7} = 3$　　　　　　　$f =$ _____

5. $\dfrac{s}{18} = 5$　　　　　　　$s =$ _____

6. $\dfrac{y}{9} = 3$　　　　　　　$y =$ _____

█ IN REAL LIFE

Suppose it is your friend's birthday. You are in charge of collecting money for the birthday cake. You know that the cake costs $12.00. You also know that there are four people (including yourself) who want to help pay. How much should each person pay? If you think of this problem as an algebraic equation, it might look like this: $4x = 12$. x is the amount of money each person must pay. It is the unknown number. Now solve the equation. Divide both sides by 4 to get the x by itself. $\frac{4x}{4} = \frac{12}{4}$. $x = 3$. Now you know that each person should pay $3.00!

Solving Two-Step Equations

In some equations, the variable is part of two or more different operations.

Look at the example below.

Example 1

$$4x - 8 = 12$$

In this equation, 4 is multiplied by x. Then 8 is subtracted from the product of 4 and x. You still need to get the variable by itself. What do you do first?

> **Rule for Solving Two-Step Equations**
>
> If there are parentheses—( )—in an equation, always do the operation in parentheses first. When there is more than one operation and there are no parentheses, do the steps below:
>
> **1.** Take care of any addition or subtraction operations.
>
> **2.** Take care of any multiplication or division operations.

Example 2

Let's work through the following equation.

$$4x - 8 = 12$$

Step 1. First, take care of any addition or subtraction operations. Add 8 to both sides.

$$4x - 8 + 8 = 12 + 8$$

$$4x = 20$$

Step 2. Take care of any multiplication or division operations.

$$\frac{4x}{4} = \frac{20}{4}$$

$$x = 5$$

Now let's look at another example.

Example 3

$$\frac{x}{3} + 65 = 120$$

Step 1. Take care of any addition or subtraction operations. Subtract 65 from both sides of the equation.

$$\frac{x}{3} + 65 - 65 = 120 - 65$$

$$\frac{x}{3} = 55$$

Step 2. Take care of any multiplication or division operations. Multiply both sides by 3 to solve for x.

$$\frac{x}{3}(3) = 55(3)$$

$$x = 165$$

■ PRACTICE 19: Solving Two-Step Equations

Solve each equation below. Write your answer on the line.

Example:

$$2z - 5 = 11$$

$$2z - 5 + 5 = 11 + 5$$

$$2z = 16$$

$$\frac{2z}{2} = \frac{16}{2}$$

$$z = 8$$

1. $\dfrac{w}{7} + 12 = 33$ $w =$ _____

2. $\dfrac{m}{6} - 8 = 14$ $m =$ _____

3. $2p + 11 = 47$ $p =$ _____

4. $7 + \dfrac{t}{6} = 15$ $t =$ _____

Combining Like Terms

In Lesson 4, you learned about combining like terms in algebraic expressions. This is often part of solving an equation. Sometimes an equation has like terms on both sides of the equal sign. When this happens, the first step in solving the equation is to collect the like terms together on one side of the equation. Look at the following example.

Example 1

$$2t + 7 = 21 - 5t$$

There are two t terms in this example—$2t$ and $5t$. They are on opposite sides of the equation. There are also two constant terms—7 and 21. **Constant** terms are terms that have no variables. Their value remains constant. You want all the t terms on one side of the equation, and all the constant terms on the other side. You need to collect the like terms.

Step 1. The first rule for solving algebra problems says that you can do anything to an equation as long as you do the same thing to both sides. To get the t terms on one side, you could either subtract $2t$ from both sides, or add $5t$ to both sides. Let's add $5t$ to both sides.

$$2t + 5t + 7 = 21 - 5t + 5t$$
$$7t + 7 = 21$$

Step 2. Now that you have all the t terms on the same side of the equation, you want to get all the constants on the other side. To do this, subtract 7 from both sides of the equation.

$$7t + 7 - 7 = 21 - 7$$
$$7t = 14$$

Step 3. Next, look at what is being done to the variable. It is being multiplied by 7. What is the opposite of multiplying by 7? It is dividing by 7. To find the value of t, you need to divide both sides by 7.

$$\frac{7t}{7} = \frac{14}{7} = 2 \qquad t = 2$$

Example 2

Here is another equation with like terms.

$$5x + 2 - 3x = 14 - 4x$$

Step 1. The left side of the equation has two x terms ($5x$ and $-3x$). Combine them: $5x - 3x = 2x$.

$$2x + 2 = 14 - 4x$$

Step 2. Now you have $2x$ on one side of the equation. You also have $-4x$ on the other side. Move the $-4x$ to the same side as the $2x$. To do this, add $4x$ to both sides of the equation.

$$2x + 4x + 2 = 14 - 4x + 4x$$
$$6x + 2 = 14$$

Step 3. Now, take care of any addition or subtraction operations. Subtract 2 from both sides.

$$6x + 2 - 2 = 14 - 2$$
$$6x = 12$$

Step 4. Finally, take care of any multiplication or division operations. Divide both sides by 6.

$$\frac{6x}{6} = \frac{12}{6}$$
$$x = 2$$

Look at the equation below.

$$2x + 2 = 14 - 4x$$

You want to combine like terms. In this equation, there are 2 "x" terms ($2x$ and $4x$). Should you subtract $2x$ from both sides, or add $4x$ to both sides? Write your answer on a separate sheet of paper.

■ PRACTICE 20: Combining Like Terms

Combine like terms. Then solve each equation. Write your answer on the line next to each equation.

Example:

$$2x - 17 + x = 43 - 3x$$

$$3x - 17 = 43 - 3x$$

$$3x + 3x - 17 = 43 - 3x + 3x$$

$$6x - 17 + 17 = 43 + 17$$

$$\frac{6x}{6} = \frac{60}{6}$$

$$x = 10$$

1. $t + t + t + 3t = 6 + 4t$ $t = $ _____

2. $7x = 9 + 4x$ $x = $ _____

3. $10n = 35 + 3n$ $n = $ _____

4. $10b + 8b - 6b = 24$ $b = $ _____

Solving Equations with Fractional Coefficients

Numbers in front of variables are called coefficients. So far, you have only worked with coefficients that are whole numbers. In some equations, the coefficient is a fraction. Look at the example below.

Example 1

$$\frac{2}{3}x = 12$$

Notice that the number before x is a fraction $\left(\frac{2}{3}\right)$. You still want to get x by itself to solve the equation. To do this, multiply both sides of the equation by the **reciprocal** of the fraction. The reciprocal of a fraction is the number that, when multiplied by the fraction, gives a product of 1. To get the reciprocal of a fraction, switch its **numerator**—the number on the top—and **denominator**—the number on the bottom. For example, the reciprocal of $\frac{2}{3}$ is $\frac{3}{2}$. The reciprocal of $\frac{5}{7}$ is $\frac{7}{5}$. A fraction multiplied by its reciprocal always equals 1. Look at the examples below.

$$\frac{5}{6}\left(\frac{6}{5}\right) = \frac{30}{30} = 1$$

$$\frac{3}{25}\left(\frac{25}{3}\right) = \frac{75}{75} = 1$$

Now look back at the equation on page 67: $\frac{2}{3}x = 12$. To get the x by itself, multiply both sides by the reciprocal of $\frac{2}{3}$, $\frac{3}{2}$.

$$\frac{3}{2}\left(\frac{2}{3}x\right) = 12\left(\frac{3}{2}\right)$$

$$x = \frac{36}{2}$$

$$x = 18$$

Example 2

Let's look at another equation with a fractional coefficient.

$$\frac{4}{5}x = 20$$

To get the x by itself, multiply both sides of the equation by the fraction's reciprocal.

$$\frac{4}{5}x\left(\frac{5}{4}\right) = 20\left(\frac{5}{4}\right)$$

$$x = \frac{100}{4}$$

$$x = 25$$

THINK ABOUT IT

You just learned that when you have a fractional coefficient, you should multiply both sides of the equation by the reciprocal of that fraction. For example, look at this equation: $\frac{1}{2}x = 4$. To solve this equation, you would multiply both sides by the reciprocal of $\frac{1}{2}$, which is $\frac{2}{1}$. $\left(\frac{2}{1}\right)\frac{1}{2}x = \left(\frac{2}{1}\right)4$. $x = 8$. Why do you think you must use the reciprocal of the fraction to solve this equation? Write your answer on a separate sheet of paper.

■ PRACTICE 21: Solving Equations with Fractional Coefficients

Solve each equation below. Write your answer on the line after each equation. Remember to take care of addition and subtraction operations before multiplication and division operations.

Example:

$$\frac{5}{6}z = 25$$

$$\left(\frac{6}{5}\right)\frac{5}{6}z = \left(\frac{6}{5}\right)25$$

$$z = \frac{150}{5}$$

$$z = 30$$

1. $\dfrac{3}{4}m = 15$ $m = $ _____

2. $\dfrac{2}{3}q + 4 = 22$ $q = $ _____

3. $\dfrac{2}{7}b + 18 = 22$ $b = $ _____

4. $\dfrac{4}{9}t = 64$ $t = $ _____

Solving Equations with Squared Variables

In many equations, you must multiply a variable by itself. Variables multiplied by themselves are called **squared variables.** For example, $x(x) = x^2$ is a squared variable. The small raised 2 is called an **exponent.** It shows how many times the variable has been multiplied by itself. An exponent of 2 means the variable is squared, or multiplied by itself once. It is the same as writing $(x)(x)$. An exponent of 3 would mean that the variable is **cubed,** or $(x)(x)(x)$. The number that, multiplied by itself, results in a squared number is called the **square root.** The symbol for "square root" is $\sqrt{}$. For example, 16 is a square number. It can be written as the product of $(4)(4)$. So 4 is the square root of 16—the number that, multiplied by itself, has a product of 16. We can write this as $\sqrt{16} = 4$. x is the square root of x^2. We can write this as $\sqrt{x^2} = x$. You can use the Table of Squares and Square Roots on pages 257–260 to find the square roots of numbers up to 100. Also, many calculators have a key to find the square root of a number.

Example 1

In the equation below, the variable is squared. It has an exponent of 2.

$$3x^2 = 48$$

You still need to get x by itself to solve the equation. You can get rid of a squared variable by taking the square root of the variable. When you take the square root of both sides of the equation, the equation will remain true.

Step 1. First, get the x by itself. Notice that x is being multiplied by 3. To get x by itself, you need to do the inverse operation. You need to divide both sides by 3. (Remember, you can do anything to an equation as long as you do the same thing to both sides.)

$$\frac{3x^2}{3} = \frac{48}{3}$$

$$x^2 = 16$$

Step 2. Since x^2 is $(x)(x)$, and both sides of the equation are equal, 16 must be some number multiplied by itself. To find the value of x, take the square root of both sides of the equation. You can use a calculator or the table on pages 257–260 to find the square root of 16.

$$\sqrt{x^2} = \sqrt{16}$$

$$x = 4$$

Look at another example.

Example 2

$$y^2 + 9 = 90$$

Step 1. First, take care of the addition operation. Subtract 9 from both sides of the equation.

$$y^2 + 9 - 9 = 90 - 9$$

$$y^2 = 81$$

Step 2. To find the value of y, take the square root of both sides of the equation.

$$\sqrt{y^2} = \sqrt{81}$$

$$y = 9$$

■ PRACTICE 22: Solving Equations with Squared Variables

Solve each equation below. Write each answer on the line. Use a calculator or the table on pages 257–260 to find the square roots of the constants.

Example:

$$2r^2 - 6 = 44$$

$$2r^2 - 6 + 6 = 44 + 6$$

$$2r^2 = 50$$

$$\frac{2r^2}{2} = \frac{50}{2}$$

$$r^2 = 25$$

$$\sqrt{r^2} = \sqrt{25}$$

$$r = 5$$

1. $m^2 + 9 = 58$ $m =$ _____

2. $7e^2 = 28$ $e =$ _____

3. $d^2 + 6 = 70$ $d =$ _____

4. $\dfrac{1}{2}n^2 - 10 = 62$ $n =$ _____

Solving Equations with Parentheses

Sometimes you will see parentheses ( ) in an equation with a number outside the parentheses. This tells you that each term inside the parentheses must be multiplied by the term(s) just outside the parentheses.

Look at the example below.

Example 1

$$6(2x + 3) = 39$$

In this example, 6 is right outside the parentheses. 6 must be multiplied by both of the terms inside the parentheses ($2x$ and 3).

$$6(2x) + 6(3) = 39$$

$$12x + 18 = 39$$

The first term, $12x$, comes from multiplying $6(2x)$. The second term, 18, comes from multiplying $6(3)$.

Let's try another example.

Example 2

$$2x(8x - 4) = 60$$

To solve this equation, you must first multiply $2x$ by both terms inside the parentheses.

$$2x(8x) - 2x(4) = 60$$

$$16x^2 - 8x = 60$$

The first term, $16x^2$, comes from multiplying $2x(8x)$. Remember, if you multiply a variable by the same variable, you get a squared variable (x times $x = x^2$). The second term, $8x$, comes from multiplying $2x$ by 4.

Solving Equations with Parentheses

Remember, before you can solve any equation that has parentheses, you must multiply the terms inside the parentheses by the term(s) just outside the parentheses.

Look at the example below.

Example 3

$$2(x-5) + 6x = 14$$

Step 1. Multiply both terms inside the parentheses by 2.

$$2(x) - 2(5) + 6x = 14$$

$$2x - 10 + 6x = 14$$

Step 2. Then, collect like terms.

$$2x - 10 + 6x = 14$$

$$8x - 10 = 14$$

Step 3. Next, get the variable by itself on one side of the equation. Add 10 to both sides.

$$8x - 10 + 10 = 14 + 10$$

$$8x = 24$$

Step 4. Look at what is being done to the variable. To get x alone, do the opposite—the inverse operation—to both sides. Divide both sides by 8.

$$\frac{8x}{8} = \frac{24}{8}$$

$$x = 3$$

Example 4

An equation may contain two or more parentheses.

$$12(b + 2) - 3 = -3(2 - b)$$

Step 1. To solve this equation, you must first multiply both terms inside the parentheses on the left side of the equation by 12. Then simplify by combining like terms.

$$12(b) + 12(2) - 3 = -3(2 - b)$$
$$12b + 24 - 3 = -3(2 - b)$$
$$12b + 21 = -3(2 - b)$$

Step 2. Now go to the right side of the equation. Multiply both terms inside the parentheses by -3.

$$12b + 21 = -3(2) - (-3)(b)$$
$$12b + 21 = -6 + 3b$$

Remember, if you multiply or divide a negative number by a positive number, you will get a negative number. If you multiply or divide two negative numbers, you will get a positive number.

Step 3. Collect like terms. Subtract $3b$ from both sides of the equation.

$$12b + 21 - 3b = -6 + 3b - 3b$$
$$9b + 21 = -6$$

Step 4. Get the variable by itself on one side of the equation. Subtract 21 from both sides of the equation.

$$9b + 21 - 21 = -6 - 21$$
$$9b = -27$$

Step 5. Look at what is being done to the variable. To get x alone, do the inverse operation to both sides of the equation. Divide both sides of the equation by 9.

$$\frac{9b}{9} = \frac{-27}{9}$$

$$b = -3$$

TIP

Whenever you multiply terms inside parentheses, remember to pay attention to the positive and negative sign before each term. For example, look at the equation $5(x - 3) = 35$. First, multiply $5(x) = 5x$. Then multiply $5(-3)$. Notice that the 3 has a negative sign in front. You must remember this sign when you multiply: $5(-3) = -15$. The final equation is $5x - 15 = 35$.

■ PRACTICE 23: Solving Equations with Parentheses

Solve each equation on the next page. Write each answer on the line.

Example:

$$5(x + 3) = 60$$

$$5(x) + 5(3) = 60$$

$$5x + 15 = 60$$

$$5x + 15 - 15 = 60 - 15$$

$$5x = 45$$

$$\frac{5x}{5} = \frac{45}{5}$$

$$x = 9$$

1. $-6(2s - 1) = 30$ $\qquad$ $s =$ _____

2. $-3m = -5(m - 8)$ $\qquad$ $m =$ _____

3. $7(2 - g) = 49$ $\qquad$ $g =$ _____

4. $-7(3w + 4) = 14$ $\qquad$ $w =$ _____

The Distance Formula

You can use the skills you have learned so far to turn formulas into algebraic equations. A **formula** is like a recipe written with variables. It asks you for certain ingredients to find a final answer. If you can replace enough variables with numbers, you can use them to find the value of the last variable.

One formula that you may find useful is the **distance formula.** If you walk 3 miles an hour for 2 hours, you will have walked 6 miles. This relationship between distance (D), rate or speed (r), and time (t) is called the distance formula:

$$D = r(t)$$

You can use this formula to find out how fast something is going (rate, sometimes called speed). You can also use it to find out how long it takes to go a certain distance (time). Lastly, you can use it to find out how far something has gone (distance). Read the problem on the next page. You can solve this problem by using the distance formula.

Example 1

Wind can push a plane faster than the measured speed it is flying. For example, a plane may be going 300 mph (miles per hour) with winds of 40 mph. This plane is actually flying at 340 mph! Suppose a plane is flying from New York to Iceland. The plane is going 500 mph, according to its speedometer. There is a wind of 40 mph. If it takes the plane 5 hours to reach Iceland, how far did the plane travel?

Step 1. First, decide what the problem wants you to find. This problem asks you to find the distance (D) the plane traveled.

Step 2. Next, you need to find the plane's rate, or speed. Because of the wind, the plane was actually flying faster than 500 mph. Add 40 mph to 500 mph. The plane was flying at 540 mph. This was the plane's rate. Put this number in the formula for r.

$$D = r(t)$$
$$D = 540(t)$$

Step 3. It took the plane 5 hours to reach Iceland. This is the time. Put this number in the formula for t.

$$D = 540(t)$$
$$D = 540(5)$$

Step 4. You now have an equation with one variable, or unknown number, D. Now, multiply to find D.

$$D = 540(5)$$
$$D = 2700$$

The plane traveled 2700 miles.

Example 2

Let's try another problem. Read the problem below.

A plane traveled from New York to Iceland in 5 hours. The trip is 2700 miles and the wind was 40 miles per hour. How fast was the plane flying according to its speedometer?

Step 1. In this problem, you want to know how fast the plane was flying (its rate). Because you want to find the value for r, you must change the formula so that r is by itself on one side of the equation. Change the formula so that rate is by itself. Divide both sides of the equation by time (t).

$$D = r(t)$$

$$\frac{D}{t} = \frac{r(t)}{t}$$

$$\frac{D}{t} = r$$

Because you did the same thing to both sides of the equation, you did not really change the equation. $\frac{D}{t} = r$ is just another way of writing $D = rt$.

Step 2. Put the information from the problem into the new formula. Remember, the wind makes the plane go faster, so add 40 to r.

$$\frac{D}{t} = r$$

$$\frac{2700}{5} = r + 40$$

$$540 = r + 40$$

Step 3. Get *r* by itself. Subtract 40 from both sides of the equation.

$$540 - 40 = r + 40 - 40$$
$$500 = r$$

The plane was traveling at 500 mph.

TIP

When you use formulas, it doesn't matter which variable remains unknown. As long as you know the value of two out of three variables, you can always find the third.

IN REAL LIFE

You can use the distance formula to find how long a trip will take. You plan to visit some friends who live 210 miles away. You drive an average of 60 miles per hour. How long will the trip take?

To find the time it will take, change the distance formula so that *t* is by itself.

$$D = r(t)$$
$$\frac{D}{r} = \frac{r(t)}{r}$$
$$\frac{D}{r} = t$$

The distance (*D*) you will travel is 210 miles. You will travel at an average rate (*r*) of 60 mph. Put this information into the formula.

$$\frac{210}{60} = t$$
$$3.5 = t$$

The trip will take you 3.5 hours.

■ PRACTICE 24: The Distance Formula

Use the distance formula to solve each problem below. Write your answer on the line after each problem.

Distance formula: $D = r(t)$

1. A car traveled 518 miles in 7 hours. What was its average rate?

   $r =$ _____ mph

2. A biker has an average speed (rate) of 15 mph. How long will it take her to travel 52.5 miles?

   $t =$ _____ hours

Setting Up Algebraic Equations

Some algebra word problems do not give you a formula. Instead, they may ask you to make a formula from the information given. This means that you must read the information very carefully.

Example 1

Read the problem below.

Janice was born 14 years after Han. Miguel is half Janice's age. Sari is as old as Miguel, Han, and Janice combined. Write a formula for Sari's age. Use Janice's age as the unknown variable. Then use this formula to find Sari's age if Janice is 16 years old.

To solve this problem, follow these steps.

Step 1. Put the information into a formula. You know that Sari's age equals the age of Miguel plus the age of Han plus the age of Janice. Use the first letter of each name as the variable to stand for that person's age.

$$S = M + H + J$$

Step 2. You know that Han is 14 years older than Janice:

$$H = 14 + J$$

Step 3. You also know that Miguel is half Janice's age:

$$M = \frac{1}{2}(J) \longrightarrow M = \frac{J}{2}$$

Step 4. Put this information into your formula.

$$S = M + H + J$$

$$S = \frac{J}{2} + 14 + J + J$$

Step 5. Combine like terms.

$$S = 2J + 14 + \frac{J}{2}$$

To add $2J$ and $\frac{J}{2}$, change $2J$ to a fraction with a denominator of 2.

$$2J \longrightarrow \frac{4J}{2}$$

$$\frac{4J}{2} + \frac{J}{2} = \frac{5J}{2}$$

$$S = \frac{5J}{2} + 14$$

Step 6. Now use your formula to find Sari's age. You know that Janice is 16 years old ($J = 16$). Put this value into your formula.

$$S = \frac{5(16)}{2} + 14$$

$$S = \frac{80}{2} + 14$$

$$S = 40 + 14$$

$$S = 54$$

Sari is 54 years old.

■ PRACTICE 25: Setting Up Algebraic Equations

Write a formula for the problem below.

The population of City E is 2 times bigger than that of City D. The population of City F is 2 times bigger than that of City E. Write a formula for the relationship between the populations of City F and City D. Then, use the formula to find the population of City F if City D has a population of 100,000.

Formula: _____

Population of City F = _____

LESSON 6: Solving Inequalities

 GOAL: To learn to solve for variables in inequalities

WORDS TO KNOW

inequality   **inequality symbol**   **simplify**

What Is an Inequality?

As you already know, an equation tells you that two
mathematical quantities are equal. Equations always use the
equal sign, =. The example below is an equation.

$$20 + 8 = 28$$

This equation tells you that 20 plus 8 equals 28.

An **inequality** is different. It tells you that the left side of a
mathematical expression may not be equal to the right side. The
example below is an inequality that uses the symbol <, is less than.

$$20 + 8 < 30$$

This inequality tells you that 20 plus 8 is less than 30.

Look at the **inequality symbols** and examples below.

Inequality Symbols	
Symbol	**Example**
≠ is not equal to	$3 \neq 4$
< is less than	$3 < 4$
> is greater than	$4 > 3$
≤ is less than or equal to	$3 \leq 4, 4 \leq 4$
≥ is greater than or equal to	$4 \geq 3, 4 \geq 4$

Unit 2: Solving Equations and Inequalities • Algebra

The symbols ≤ and ≥ are like either-or statements. ≤ means, "either these two expressions are equal, or the one on the left is less than the one on the right." ≥ means, "either these two expressions are equal, or the one on the left is greater than the one on the right."

Suppose someone asks you where your jacket is. You say that it is either in the car or in your room. The jacket turns out to be in your room. Was your statement true? Yes, it was. It would also have been true if the jacket had been in the car. The statement would only be false if the jacket was neither in the car nor in your room.

In the same way, statements that use ≤ are true either if the expressions are equal or if the one on the left is less than the one on the right. Statements that use ≥ are true either if the expressions are equal or if the one on the left is greater than the one on the right.

Look at the following example.

Example 1

$$7 \leq 9$$

This example tells you that 7 is less than or equal to 9. Is this true? You know that 7 is less than 9. This statement is true.

Look at another example.

Example 2

$$5 \geq 5$$

This statement is true. 5 is equal to 5.

Now look at the example below.

Example 3

$$5 \le 3$$

Is this example true? 5 is not less than 3. It is also not equal to 3. 5 is greater than 3. Therefore, this statement is false.

When you look at two numbers, you can use a number line to tell which number is smaller or larger. The smaller numbers are to the left on the number line. The larger numbers are to the right on the number line. If one number is to the left of another number, it is smaller than (<) that number. If one number is to the right of another number, it is greater than (>) that number.

Look at the following example.

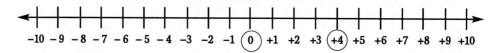

In the example above, 4 and 0 are circled. 0 is to the left of 4. That means that 0 is less than 4.

$$0 < 4$$

Look at another example.

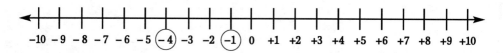

In the example, −1 is to the right of −4 on the number line. This means that −1 is greater than −4.

$$-1 > -4$$

TIP

When you see a "greater than" (>) or "less than" (<) symbol, remember that the pointed end of the sign always faces the smaller number. Think of the inequality signs as arrows that point to the smaller number. This way you will always know which number is smaller and which is greater!

■ PRACTICE 26: Inequality Symbols

Look at the statements below. Circle *a* if the equation is true. Circle *b* if it is false.

1. $3 < 22$
    a. true   **b.** false

2. $-4 > 4$
    a. true   **b.** false

3. $0 > -3$
    a. true   **b.** false

4. $6 \neq 7$
    a. true   **b.** false

5. $15 > 15$
    a. true   **b.** false

6. $-5 \leq -5$
    a. true   **b.** false

Write the correct inequality symbol for each statement below.

Example:

$$25 > 22$$

7. −4 _____ − 8

8. 0 _____ −10

9. 6 _____ $\dfrac{18}{6}$

10. 14 _____ 15

11. −5 _____ 5

12. 15 _____ 0

13. 12 _____ 16

14. $\dfrac{4}{2}$ _____ $\dfrac{2}{2}$

Inequalities with Variables

You can use variables in an inequality. When you write $d \leq 5$, d stands for all numbers less than or equal to 5. To show $d \leq 5$ on a number line, place a filled-in circle over 5. Then draw a line toward the left with an arrow at the left end. The filled-in circle means that 5 is one possible value of d. The arrow means that any number to the left of 5 is also a possible value.

$$d \le 5$$

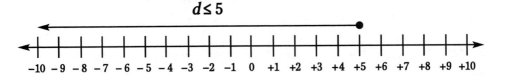

You can represent $y > -2$ by putting an empty circle above -2. Then draw a line to the right with an arrow at the end. The empty circle means that -2 is not included in the solution, since y is greater than -2 but not equal to -2.

$$y > -2$$

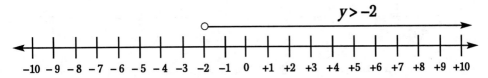

Drawing Number Lines

- To show that a number is included in the solution set, draw a filled-in circle on the number line.

- To show that a number is not included in the solution set, draw an open circle on the number line.

■ THINK ABOUT IT

Look at the number line below:

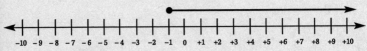

Does this number line mean the same thing as $y > -2$? Write your answer on a separate sheet of paper.

■ PRACTICE 27: Inequalities with Variables

Do each exercise that follows.

Example: Show the inequality $s > 4$ on the number line below.

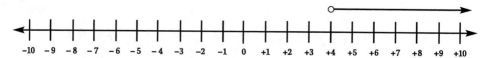

1. Show the inequality $f < -4$ on the number line below.

2. Show the inequality $k \geq 0$ on the number line below.

3. Look at the number lines below. Which one shows the inequality $x \geq 3$?

   a.

   b.

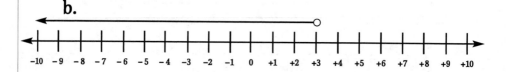

   c.

   d.

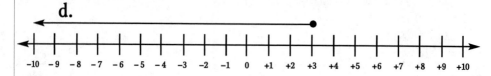

4. Look at the number lines below. Which one shows the inequality $x < -5$?

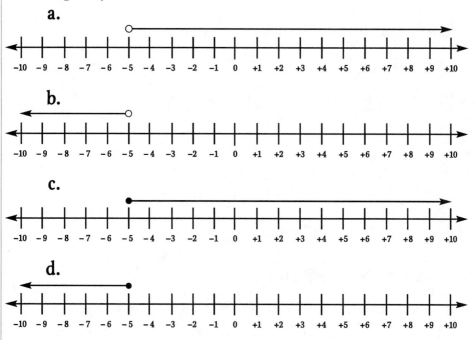

a.

b.

c.

d.

Rules for Inequalities

In the first part of this book, you learned the rules for working with equations. Now you will learn the rules for working with inequalities.

> ### Rule 1 for Inequalities
>
> You can add or subtract the same number to or from each side of the inequality, and it will still be true.

Example 1

Add ten to both sides of the following inequality.

$$14 < 15$$

$$14 + 10 < 15 + 10$$

$$24 < 25$$

The inequality is still true.

Example 2

Subtract 2 from both sides of the following inequality.

$$8 > -3$$

$$8 - 2 > -3 - 2$$

$$6 > -5$$

The inequality is still true.

Rule 2 for Inequalities

You can multiply or divide each side of an inequality by the same positive number and the inequality will still be true.

Example 3

Multiply both sides of the following inequality by 2.

$$5 < 8$$

$$5(2) < 8(2)$$

$$10 < 16$$

The inequality is still true.

Example 4

Divide both sides of the following inequality by 3.

$$24 > 9$$

$$\frac{24}{3} > \frac{9}{3}$$

$$8 > 3$$

The inequality is still true.

Rule 3 for Inequalities

You can multiply or divide an inequality by a negative number, but you must change the direction of the inequality sign.

Example 5

Multiply both sides of the following inequality by –2.

$$12 > 8$$

$12(-2)$ is -24. $8(-2)$ is -16. -24 is less than -16. To make the statement true, change the inequality sign from > to <.

$$12(-2) < 8(-2)$$

$$-24 < -16$$

Example 6

Rule 3 says that you must also change the direction of the inequality sign when you divide. In the example below, both sides of the inequality are to be divided by –11.

$$33 < 55$$

$$\frac{33}{-11} < \frac{55}{-11}$$

$$\frac{33}{-11} = -3 \qquad \frac{55}{-11} = -5$$

$\dfrac{33}{-11}$, or –3, is greater than $\dfrac{55}{-11}$, or –5. To make the statement true, you must change the inequality sign from < to >.

$$-3 > -5$$

■ PRACTICE 28: Rules for Inequalities

Solve each problem below. Write each answer on the line.

Example: Multiply both sides of 4 < 7 by –3. –12 > –21

$$4(-3) > 7(-3)$$

$$-12 > -21$$

1. Add –4 to both sides of 9 > –5. _____

2. Subtract 10 from both sides of –3 < –2. _____

3. Multiply both sides of 8 < 10 by –1. _____

4. Divide both sides of –20 < –10 by –10. _____

5. Divide both sides of 4 > –2 by –2. _____

6. Multiply both sides of 5 < 6 by –3. _____

7. Multiply both sides of –3 < –1 by –4. _____

8. Subtract –5 from both sides of –10 > –15. _____

Solving Inequalities

To solve a problem with an inequality, do the same things that you do to solve equations.

Example 1

Here is a simple inequality that can be solved in one step.

$$n + 7 < 10$$

To get the variable alone on one side, subtract 7 from both sides of the inequality.

$$n + 7 - 7 < 10 - 7$$

$$n < 3$$

The solution to the inequality $n + 7 < 10$ is $n < 3$. This solution means that $n + 7$ would be less than 10 if you replaced n with any number less than three. This solution is shown on the number line below.

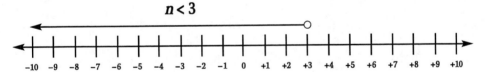

$$n < 3$$

The empty circle means that 3 is not included in the answer. The inequality states less than ($<$), not less than or equal to ($\leq$).

Example 2

Now look at the following inequality.

$$-2b > 12$$

To solve an inequality that has a variable, you must get the variable by itself on one side of the inequality sign. To get rid of the -2 in front of b in this inequality, divide both sides by -2.

Don't forget rule 3 for inequalities! Because you are dividing by a negative number, you must change the inequality sign from $>$ to $<$.

$$\frac{-2b}{-2} < \frac{12}{-2}$$

$$b < -6$$

This solution means that all numbers, including fractions, that are less than -6 will work in the inequality. Here are some numbers that would not work:

-5	-2	-0.6	0	$\dfrac{1}{6}$	3	1000

These numbers will not work because they are not less than -6.

Example 3

Look at the following inequality.

$$v - 13 \le 6$$

To get the variable alone on one side, add 13 to both sides of this inequality.

$$v - 13 + 13 \le 6 + 13$$

$$v \le 19$$

The solution includes all numbers that are less than or equal to 19.

Example 4

Now look at the following inequality.

$$\frac{1}{2}r \ge -3$$

This inequality has a fractional coefficient. (Remember, a coefficient is a number that comes right in front of a variable.) To get rid of the fractional coefficient, you must multiply both sides of the inequality by the reciprocal of the coefficient.

The reciprocal is the number that, when multiplied by the fraction, has a product of 1. To find the reciprocal, switch the numerator and the denominator of the fraction. The reciprocal of $\frac{1}{2}$ is $\frac{2}{1}$. Multiply both sides of the equation by $\frac{2}{1}$.

$$\left(\frac{1}{2}\right)\left(\frac{2}{1}\right) r \geq -3 \left(\frac{2}{1}\right)$$

$$r \geq -6$$

The solution to this inequality includes all numbers (including fractions) that are greater than or equal to –6.

IN REAL LIFE

Understanding inequalities can help you manage your money. Suppose your bank says that you must have a balance ≥ $250. Otherwise, you must pay a service charge. You have exactly $250 in the bank. Do you have to pay the service charge? Write your answer on a separate sheet of paper.

■ PRACTICE 29: Solving Inequalities

Solve each problem that follows. Write your answer on the line after each inequality.

Example: $2w > 8$

$$\frac{2w}{2} > \frac{8}{2}$$

$$w > 4$$

1. $m + 10 < 16$ _____

2. $-2g \geq 8$ _____

3. $y - 22 < 19$ _____

4. $-7b > -28$ _____

5. $h + 30 < 0$ _____

6. $-5x < 10$ _____

7. $t + 13 > 22$ _____

8. $w - 12 < 16$ _____

Solving Inequalities in Two Steps

To solve some inequalities, you need to follow two or more steps. Like equations, the basic idea is to get the variable by itself.

Example 1

Look at the example below.

$$3m - 4 > 5$$

Step 1. To solve an inequality like this one, you must get the variable alone on one side first. Add 4 to both sides.

$$3m - 4 + 4 > 5 + 4$$

$$3m > 9$$

Step 2. Now look at what is being done to the variable, and do the opposite to both sides of the equation. Divide both sides by 3.

$$\frac{3m}{3} > \frac{9}{3}$$

$$m > 3$$

The solution is $m > 3$.

Example 2

Now try another two-step inequality.

$$-2b - 8 < 12$$

Step 1. To get the variable alone on one side, add 8 to both sides of the equation.

$$-2b - 8 + 8 < 12 + 8$$

$$-2b < 20$$

Step 2. Divide both sides by –2. Since you are dividing by a negative number, you must change the inequality sign from < to >.

$$\frac{-2b}{-2} > \frac{20}{-2}$$

$$b > -10$$

The solution is $b > -10$.

■ PRACTICE 30: Solving Inequalities in Two Steps

Solve each inequality that follows. Write each answer on the line.

Example: $2w - 1 > 9$

$2w - 1 + 1 > 9 + 1$

$2w > 10$

$\dfrac{2w}{2} > \dfrac{10}{2}$

$w > 5$

1. $2m + 5 < -1$ _____

2. $-2g - 4 < 20$ _____

3. $\dfrac{y}{4} + 5 > 7$ _____

4. $-7b - 2 > -30$ _____

5. $4h - 12 < 20$ _____

6. $-6x + 3 \leq 15$ _____

7. $3r - 12 > 9$ _____

8. $-2x + 7 \leq 19$ _____

Simplifying Inequalities

You can collect like terms in inequalities, just as you can in equations. This is called **simplifying** the inequality.

Example 1

Follow these steps to solve the following inequality.

$$2s + 4s < 24$$

Step 1. This inequality has two groups of s terms, $2s$ and $4s$. Simplify the inequality by adding the s terms.

$$6s < 24$$

Step 2. Divide both sides by 6 to get the variable by itself on the left side.

$$\frac{6s}{6} < \frac{24}{6}$$

$$s < 4$$

The solution is $s < 4$.

Look at another example.

Example 2

$$4b - 27 > -5b$$

Step 1. This inequality has two *b* terms, one on each side. Simplify by adding $5b$ to both sides:

$$4b - 27 + 5b > -5b + 5b$$

$$9b - 27 > 0$$

Step 2. Get the variable on one side of the inequality, with the constant on the other side. Add 27 to both sides.

$$9b - 27 + 27 > 0 + 27$$

$$9b > 27$$

Step 3. Get the variable by itself. Divide both sides by 9.

$$\frac{9b}{9} > \frac{27}{9}$$

$$b > 3$$

The solution is $b > 3$.

Remember, the first step in solving an inequality is to simplify. Add or subtract similar terms.

THINK ABOUT IT

Look at this problem.

$$-6y > -30$$

Holly gave the following answer: $y > 5$. Is she correct? Why or why not? Write your answer on a separate sheet of paper.

■ PRACTICE 31: Simplifying Inequalities

Solve each inequality below. Write each answer on the line.

Example: $6y - 2y > 12$

$$4y > 12$$
$$\frac{4y}{4} > \frac{12}{4}$$
$$y > 3$$

1. $14k + k < 30$ _____

2. $9d - 3d + 7 > 31$ _____

3. $13x - 2x > 77$ _____

4. $5y < 7y + 18$ _____

5. $3f - 12 > -10 + 9f$ _____

6. $4t - 8 < 2t - 2$ _____

7. $15h + 16 > 6h - 20$ _____

8. $4r - 2r > 6 - r$ _____

UNIT 2 REVIEW

Solve each equation or inequality. Write your answer on the line following each one.

1. $x - 27 = 193$ $x =$ _____

2. $f(12) = 48$ $f =$ _____

3. $4s + 2 = 74$ $s =$ _____

4. $9(r + 1) - 18 = 2r + 12$ $r =$ _____

5. Tanika drove 189 miles. She drove 63 miles per hour. For how many hours did Tanika drive? $t =$ _____ hours

6. $-2x < 4$ $x =$ _____

7. $5t + 7 < 32$ $t =$ _____

8. $12s - 17 \geq 2s + 33$ $s =$ _____

9. $-8m > -24$ $m =$ _____

10. $8n + 7 > 4n + 35$ $n =$ _____

UNIT 2 APPLICATION ACTIVITY 1
Saving Your Money

You can use algebraic formulas to find many different kinds of information. In this activity, you will use a formula to help you save money.

Suppose you wanted to start saving for retirement. You want to find out about the IRA's (Individual Retirement Accounts) at many banks. You want to use the bank with the highest percentage rate. This is the rate at which your money will grow while it is in the IRA. The higher the rate, the more money you will have!

First, get information from three different banks. Ask them what their annual rate of interest is for an IRA. Then write the information on the next page.

Name of Bank	Interest Rate
1. _____	_____ %
2. _____	_____ %
3. _____	_____ %

Now use the interest formula to answer the questions below. The interest formula is interest = rate × time × principal. You already know what rate means. Time is the amount of time your money is in the IRA. Principal is the amount of money you put in the IRA. Interest is the amount of extra money you will make while your money sits in the IRA.

$$\text{Interest} = \text{rate} \times \text{time} \times \text{principal}$$

Remember to set up the formula so that the number you do not know (the variable) is by itself on one side of the equation.

Bank 1: Suppose you put $500 into an IRA at this bank. How much interest would you earn in 10 years? $_____

Bank 2: If your IRA earns $33.28 in interest in one year, how much money do you have in the IRA? $_____

Bank 3: Say you have $1800 in an IRA here. If it has earned $105 in interest, how long have you had the account?

_____

- **Optional Activity:** Choose one of the IRA accounts you researched above. What if you put $260 in this account each year? (That would only be $5 each week!) Make a graph showing how your account balance would increase each year for the next 10 years. Don't forget to add the interest!

UNIT 2 APPLICATION ACTIVITY 2
Road Trip!

Use a map with a mileage scale to plan an imaginary (or not!) road trip. Your trip should include at least four overnight stops. First, use the mileage scale to answer the following questions about your trip:

- What is the total distance you plan to travel? _____

- Where will you stop overnight? _____

- What are the distances between each stop? _____

  _____ _____ _____

- How many days do you want the trip to take? _____

   Now, use the distance formula (distance = rate × time) to answer the questions below. Remember to set up the formula so that the unknown quantity (*x*) is by itself on one side of the equation.

- You want to drive 200 miles on the first day. If you drive at 60 mph, how long will this take? _____

- You want to drive for 5 hours on the second day. If you drive at 65 mph, how far will you go? _____

- On the third day, you travel 125 miles in 2.75 hours. What is your rate of speed? _____

- Use the distance formula to find your average rate (speed) for the whole trip. _____

- **Optional Activity:** Suppose you can drive no faster than 55 mph. You have five days to drive somewhere and return. How far can you go? Find a place on the map within this distance. This place will be your destination. Then, write a travel plan for your trip. Include the number of miles you will drive each day, where you will go, how many hours you will drive each day, and where you will spend each night.

UNIT 2 APPLICATION ACTIVITY 3

The Price of Credit

When you make purchases with a credit card, you can end up paying more than you thought. In this activity, you will use algebra to find out how much something will cost if you buy it with a credit card and send in small monthly payments until you have paid for it.

Find an ad for airline tickets or call travel agents in your area to get prices for tickets to a place you would like to go. Shop around for the best deal. What is the best price you found for the tickets you want? _____

Imagine that you pay for the tickets with a credit card. The credit card has an annual interest rate of 18%. You decide to send the credit card company $20 a month until the tickets are paid for.

The credit card company charges no interest for the first month after you buy the tickets. You send the company a check for $20 when the first bill comes. You now owe the original price of the tickets minus $20. How much do you have left to pay?

_____

The next month, your bill is for the amount you found on page 106, plus an interest charge. Your annual interest rate is 18%. This means that your monthly interest rate is 18% divided by 12 (the number of months in a year). What is your monthly interest rate? _____

Your new balance (the amount you now owe) is the amount you had left to pay after you paid $20 last month *plus* the new interest that is being charged. To figure out how much this adds up to, multiply the monthly interest rate by the amount of money you still owe. This is your interest charge. Now add this interest charge to the amount you already owed. What is your total balance? _____

Suppose you keep paying $20 per month. Every month, interest is added to your balance. How many months will it take you to pay off the tickets? _____

What is the total amount, including all of the interest, that you will have paid for the tickets? _____

■ **Optional Activity:** Make a line graph that shows how your balance changes each month for the preceding activity.

UNIT 3

Graphing Linear Equations

LESSON 7: The Coordinate Plane

WORDS TO KNOW

axes	intersect	*x*-axis
axis	line	*x*-coordinate
coordinates	ordered pair	*y*-axis
coordinate plane	origin	*y*-coordinate
horizontal	vertical	

Vertical Number Lines

The number lines you have seen so far have been **horizontal** number lines. This means that they go from side to side across the page. Number lines can also be **vertical.** A vertical number line goes up and down on the page. On a vertical number line, the positive numbers are above 0 and the negative numbers are below 0. This means that to find a negative number on a vertical number line, you must look below 0. To find a positive number, you must look above 0. The numbers on a vertical number line get larger as you go up and smaller as you go down.

Example 1

Look at the vertical number lines on the next page. On the number line on the left, +3 is graphed. On the number line on the right, −2 is graphed.

 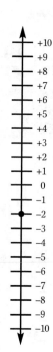

■ PRACTICE 32: Vertical Number Lines

Graph each number below on the vertical number line.

1. −5

2. 0

3. +1 $\dfrac{3}{4}$

4. −1

5. +3

6. +2.5

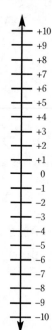

Forming the Coordinate Plane

You can overlap a horizontal number line and a vertical number line. When you do, you form a coordinate plane. Look at the diagram below. It shows a **coordinate plane.**

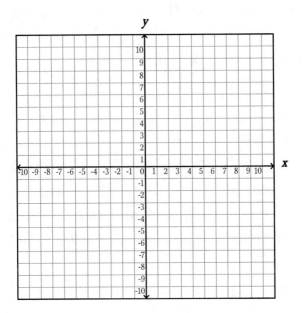

Each number line in a coordinate plane is called an **axis.** ("**Axes**" is the plural of "axis.") On a coordinate plane, the horizontal number line is called the **x-axis.** The vertical number line is called the **y-axis.** The two number lines **intersect** (cross) at the 0 point of each number line. This point is called the **origin** of the coordinate plane.

Graphing Points in a Coordinate Plane

To graph points on a coordinate plane, you need two numbers. You need a number that is on the x-axis (the horizontal number line). You also need a number that is on the y-axis (the vertical number line). These numbers are called **coordinates.** The number that is on the x-axis is called the **x-coordinate.** The number that is on the y-axis is called the **y-coordinate.** When you write these two coordinates together, you are writing an **ordered pair.** The x-coordinate tells you how far to move on the horizontal number line. The y-coordinate tells you how far to move on the vertical number line. Then you can graph the point on the coordinate plane.

There is a standard way to write an ordered pair that represents a point on the coordinate plane. That's why they're called "ordered." The order they're written in shows which number is the x-coordinate and which is the y-coordinate. Write the point's x-coordinate, then a comma, then the point's y-coordinate. Then put the whole thing in parentheses. This is an example of an ordered pair: (3, –1). So is this: (–2, –6).

Here's how to graph a point represented by an ordered pair.

1. First, find the x-coordinate on the x-axis. Is the x-coordinate a positive number? If so, look to the right of 0 on the x-axis. Is the x-coordinate a negative number? If so, look to the left of 0 on the x-axis.
2. Next, find the y-coordinate. Is the y-coordinate positive? If so, look above 0 on the y-axis. Is the y-coordinate negative? If so, look below 0 on the y-axis.
3. Then draw an imaginary line up or down from the x-coordinate.
4. Draw another imaginary line out to the left or right of the y-coordinate.
5. Put a dot where the two lines would meet.

Example

For example, say you want to graph the ordered pair (3, –2).

Step 1. First, find 3 on the *x*-axis. The number 3 is a positive number. So it is to the right of 0 on the *x*-axis.

Step 2. Then, find –2 on the *y*-axis. The number –2 is a negative number, so it is below 0 on the *y*-axis.

Step 3. Draw an imaginary line down from 3 on the *x*-axis.

Step 4. Draw another imaginary line out to the right of –2 on the *y*-axis.

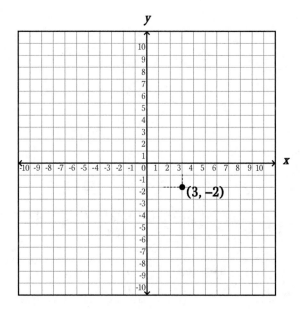

Step 5. Draw a dot where these two imaginary lines would meet.

You can see the ordered pair (3, –2) graphed on the coordinate plane above.

■ PRACTICE 33: Graphing Points on the Coordinate Plane

Graph each ordered pair below on the coordinate plane.

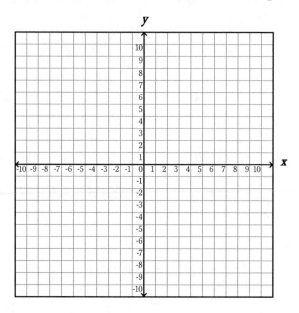

1. $(1, -5)$

2. $(-3, -2)$

3. $(-5, 2)$

4. $(3, 1)$

Graphing Lines on the Coordinate Plane

You know how to graph points on a coordinate plane. You can also use coordinates to graph lines.

In everyday terms, the word "line" can mean different things. In math, it always means one thing. A **line** is a straight set of points that continues indefinitely in both directions. To graph a line, you need to know the coordinates of at least two of the points that make up the line. Graph the points on the coordinate plane. Then draw a line that goes through both points. Finally, draw arrows on both ends of the line. The arrows show that the line doesn't stop. It goes on forever in both directions.

Example 1

Look at the two sets of ordered pairs (2, 4) and (6, 4).

Step 1. Graph the points on the coordinate plane.

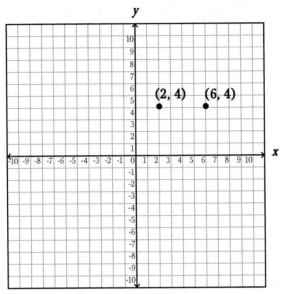

Step 2. Use a ruler to draw a straight line that goes through both points. Then draw arrows on both ends of the line to show that it goes on in both directions.

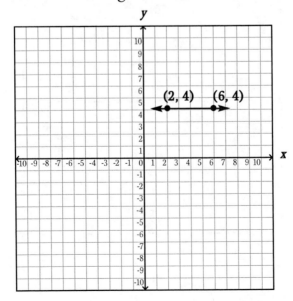

The finished graph shows a horizontal line. If you look at the *y*-coordinates, you'll see why. The *y*-coordinate for both points was 4. If two points have the same *y*-coordinate, the points are at the same distance from 0 on the *y*-axis. The line that goes through them has to be horizontal. This also means that all points on this line must have a *y*-coordinate of 4. Because the line is straight, and you know that two points have a *y*-coordinate of 4, you can tell that all other points on the line must have the same *y*-coordinate.

Example 2

Let's try another set of points. Look at the ordered pairs (2, 5) and (2, 8).

Step 1. Graph the points on the coordinate plane.

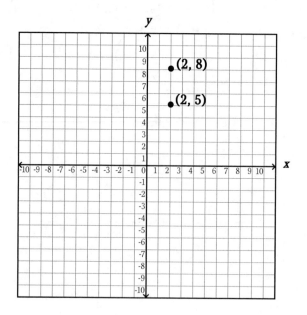

Step 2. Use a ruler to draw a straight line that goes through both points. Then draw arrows on both ends of the line to show that it goes on in both directions.

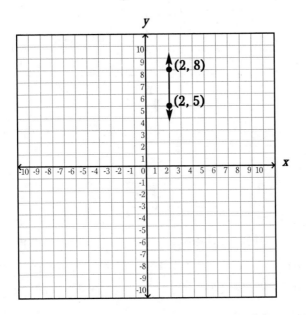

This time, the finished graph shows a vertical line. If you look at the x-coordinates, you'll see why. The x-coordinate for both points was 2. If two points have the same x-coordinate, the points are the same distance from 0 on the x-axis. The line that goes through them has to be vertical. This also means that all points on this line must have an x-coordinate of 2. Because the line is straight, and you know that two points have an x-coordinate of 2, you can tell that all other points on the line must have the same x-coordinate.

Example 3

Let's look at one more set of points. Look at the ordered pairs (2, 4) and (4, 7).

Step 1. Graph the points on the coordinate plane.

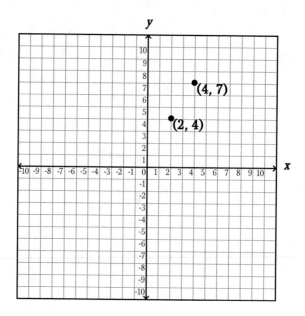

Step 2. Use a ruler to draw a straight line that goes through both points. Then draw arrows on both ends of the line to show that it goes on in both directions.

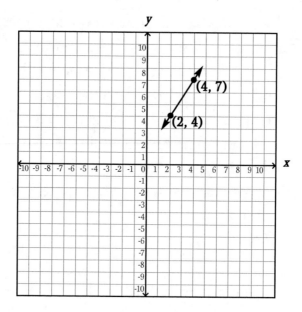

This time, the finished graph shows a line that starts low, then slants upward. The coordinates in both points are different. If both points have different coordinates, the line that goes through them will slant either up or down. This also means that no other points on this line can have the same *x*-coordinate or *y*-coordinate as either of these points. To have a point with any of these coordinates, the line would have to bend. Because the line is straight, no other points on the line can have these coordinates.

■ PRACTICE 34: Graphing Lines on the Coordinate Plane

Use the coordinate plane to graph the lines represented by each set of points below.

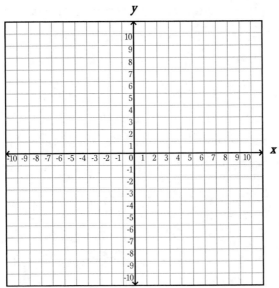

1. (1, 3) and (2, 5)

2. (–2, 4) and (–6, 1)

3. (–4, –3) and (–1, –5)

4. (3, –2) and (7, –1)

LESSON 8: Graphing Linear Equations

GOAL: To graph linear equations using the table method and the intercept method

WORDS TO KNOW

intercept method   **linear equations**

What Is a Linear Equation?

You have learned how to graph lines on a coordinate plane when you know the coordinates of at least two points on the line. You can also graph lines when you don't have the coordinates for any points. To do this, you need the equation for the line—the rule for finding the line.

Equations for lines show how the *x*-coordinate for every point on the line relates to the *y*-coordinate. These equations use variables for the *x*-coordinate and *y*-coordinate. They are usually called **linear equations,** or equations that have to do with lines.

IN REAL LIFE

Joaquin put $50 in a savings account last year. Since then, he has added $20 to the account every week. He was curious about how much his savings would add up to over time. Discounting interest, he saw that at any time his savings would equal $50 plus the number of weeks he had been saving multiplied by $20. Joaquin wrote this out as an equation, using *s* for savings and *w* for the number of weeks: $s = 50 + 20w$. Now to calculate his savings, Joaquin just has to replace *w* with the actual number of weeks he has been saving.

Look at the line on the coordinate plane below. No points are marked on the line. But if you look carefully, you can figure out what the coordinates of some of the points must be.

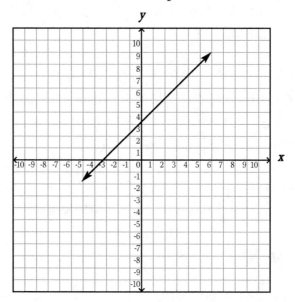

Start by marking three points on the line. Look for points where the lines of the grid cross each other. These are the easiest points to find the coordinates for.

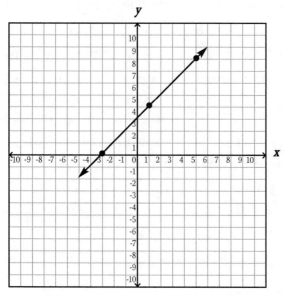

To find the coordinates, start with the point farthest to the left. To find the *x*-coordinate of this point, look at how far left or right of 0 it is on the *x*-axis. This point is 3 spaces left of 0 on the *x*-axis. This means its *x*-coordinate is −3. (Numbers to the left of 0 on the *x*-axis are negative.)

To find the *y*-coordinate of this point, look at how far above or below 0 it is on the *y*-axis. This point is level with 0 on the *y*-axis. This means its *y*-coordinate is 0. Written as an ordered pair, the coordinates of this point are (−3, 0).

Do the same thing for the other points. The second point is 1 space right of 0 and 4 spaces above 0. Its coordinates are (1, 4). The third point is 5 spaces right of 0 and 8 spaces above 0. Its coordinates are (5, 8).

Now you know the coordinates of three points on the line: (−3, 0), (1, 4), and (5, 8). Look at how the *x*-coordinate in each point relates to the *y*-coordinate. In the first pair, the *x*-coordinate is −3 and the *y*-coordinate is 0. The *y*-coordinate is 3 more than the *x*-coordinate. Now look at the second pair, 1 and 4. Again, the *y*-coordinate is 3 more than the *x*-coordinate. What about the third pair? The coordinates have the same relationship. The *y*-coordinate is 3 more than the *x*-coordinate.

Since the line is straight, you can tell that the same thing will also be true for every other point on the line. You have found the rule for the coordinates of this line. No matter what the *x*-coordinate is, you can find the *y*-coordinate by adding 3 to the *x*-coordinate. If the *x*-coordinate is 2, then the *y*-coordinate will be 2 + 3, or 5. If the *x*-coordinate is 4, then the *y*-coordinate will be 4 + 3, or 7. If you look back at the line that is graphed on page 123, you can see that this is true. The coordinate pairs (2, 5) and (4, 7) are points on the line.

You can write the rule for finding the coordinates of the line as an equation. This makes it much shorter to write. Use the variables x and y for the x-coordinate and y-coordinate. Since the rule says you can find the y-coordinate by adding 3 to the x-coordinate, you can write the equation as $y = x + 3$. This means that for any value of x, y will be $x + 3$. You have found the equation for the line, or the linear equation: $y = x + 3$.

The Table Method of Graphing Linear Equations

Now you know what linear equations are. Next, you will learn how to show these equations on the coordinate plane. One way to do this is to make a table of values for the variables in the equation. You remember that a linear equation tells how the x-coordinates of a line relate to the y-coordinates. If you choose a value for x, you can find the value for y by putting the value for x into the equation. Once you have several values for both x and y, write them as ordered pairs. Then graph the ordered pairs on the coordinate plane. The result will be a straight line—the graph of the linear equation.

Example 1

Make a table of values and graph the equation $3x + y = 2$.

Step 1. Set up a table. Write x above one column and y above the other.

x	y

Step 2. Choose several values for x. You can choose any values for x, but it is usually easiest to work with small whole numbers. Try working with -1, 0, and 1 as values for x. Write these values in the table under the x.

x	y
-1	
0	
1	

Step 3. For each value of x, you need to find the corresponding value of y. To do this, substitute each value for x in the equation. Start with $x = -1$.

$$3x + y = 2$$

$$3(-1) + y = 2$$

$$-3 + y = 2$$

Step 4. Get y by itself on one side of the equation. In this case, add 3 to both sides.

$$(-3 + 3) + y = 2 + 3$$

$$y = 5$$

Step 5. Now you know that when $x = -1$, $y = 5$. Write 5 in the table under y, on the same row as -1.

x	y
-1	5
0	
1	

Step 6. Do the same for the other values of x in the table.

$x = 0$

$3(0) + y = 2$

$0 + y = 2$

$y = 2$

$x = 1$

$3(1) + y = 2$

$(3 - 3) + y = 2 - 3$

$y = -1$

Step 7. Write each value for y in the table.

x	y
-1	5
0	2
1	-1

Step 8. Write the values in the table as ordered pairs. The x-values will be the x-coordinates. The y-values will be the y-coordinates.

$(-1, 5), (0, 2), (1, -1)$

Step 9. Graph the ordered pairs on a coordinate plane. Draw a straight line that connects all three of the points.

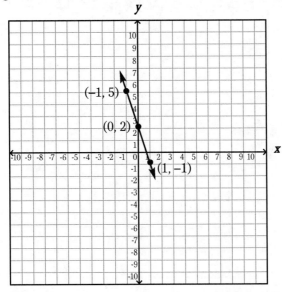

The points that you graph from the solutions for a linear equation should always form a straight line. There are an infinite number of solutions to a linear equation. Why do you think that you draw your line using three possible solutions instead of one or two or ten or fifty? Write your answer on a separate sheet of paper.

■ PRACTICE 35: The Table Method of Graphing Linear Equations

Use the table method to graph the linear equation in problem 1 on the coordinate plane.

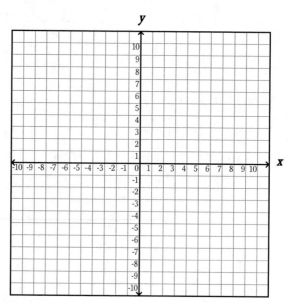

1. $2x + y = -3$

x	y

The Intercept Method of Graphing Linear Equations

There is another way of graphing a linear equation. With this method, you draw a line using only two points on the coordinate plane. This is called the **intercept method** of graphing linear equations.

Here's how to use the intercept method. You find the two points where the line of the linear equation meets (intersects with) the axes of the coordinate plane. Then draw a straight line through these two points.

First, you need to find the two points where the line of the linear equation intersects with the axes of the coordinate plane. To do this, you must find the value for y when x equals 0. You must also find the value for x when y equals 0.

Example 1

Look at the linear equation below.

$$-2x + y = 4$$

We will use the intercept method to graph the line of the linear equation above.

Step 1. Find the value for y when x equals 0 by substituting 0 for x.

$$-2(0) + y = 4$$

$$0 + y = 4$$

$$y = 4$$

Step 2. Now, find the value for *x* when *y* equals 0. To do this, start by substituting 0 for *y*.

$$-2x + 0 = 4$$

$$-2x = 4$$

Step 3. Divide both sides by –2 to get *x* by itself on one side of the equation.

$$\frac{-2x}{-2} = \frac{4}{-2}$$

$$x = -2$$

Step 4. Make your solutions into ordered pairs. The *x* value is the *x*-coordinate. The *y* value is the *y*-coordinate.

(–2, 0)

(0, 4)

Step 5. Graph the two points on the coordinate plane. Draw a straight line that goes through both of them.

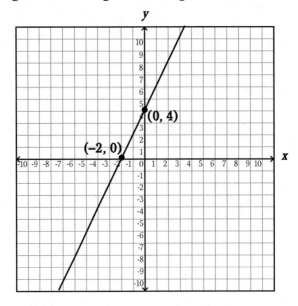

■ PRACTICE 36: The Intercept Method of Graphing Linear Equations

Use the intercept method to graph each linear equation on its coordinate plane.

1. $3x - 2y = 12$

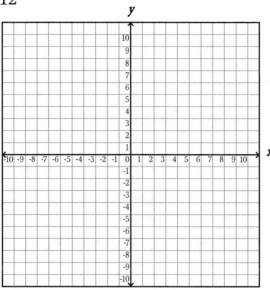

2. $5x + 3y = 15$

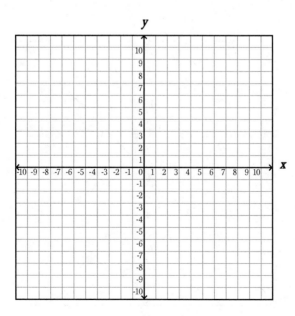

LESSON 9: Slope

GOAL: To learn to find the slope of a line and to use a slope to graph lines

WORDS TO KNOW

ratio   slope

Finding Linear Slope

Slope is the steepness of the slant of a line. It is the number of *y*-units a line goes up or down when it moves over one *x*-unit.

The slope for line A in the diagram below is 1. This means that as the line moves over one space, it moves up one space. For example, as the line moves from 0 to 1 on the *x*-axis, it rises from 0 to 1 on the *y*-axis. This means that line A has a slope of 1.

The slope for line B in the diagram below is much steeper. As it moves from 0 to 1 on the *x*-axis, it rises from 0 to 3 on the *y*-axis. This means that line B has a slope of 3.

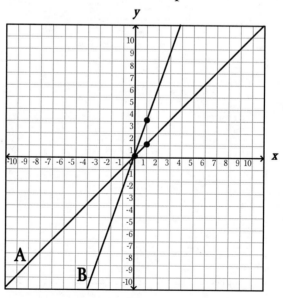

The symbol for slope is *m*. For line A on the previous page, *m* = 1. For line B, *m* = 3.

THINK ABOUT IT

Slope is a **ratio.** This means that it is a relationship between two things. What two things about a line must be related to each other to find the line's slope? Write your answer on a separate sheet of paper.

■ PRACTICE 37: Finding Linear Slope

Find the slope for the line below. Write your answer on the line at the right of the diagram.

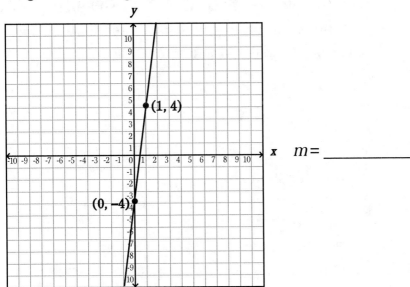

$$m = \underline{\hspace{2cm}}$$

The Formula for Finding Slope

You can find the slope for any line if you know the coordinates of two points on the line. The formula below is the formula for finding slope:

$$m = \frac{(y2 - y1)}{(x2 - x1)}$$

In the formula on page 133, $y2$ means the y-coordinate of the second point of the line whose slope you are trying to find. In the formula, $y1$ means the y-coordinate of the first point of the line whose slope you are trying to find. Also, $x2$ is the x-coordinate of the second point of the line. Finally, $x1$ is the x-coordinate of the first point of the line.

Example 1

Use this formula to find the slope of a line with the points (2, 1) and (6, 4). To do this, follow the steps below.

Step 1. Choose which point you want to be point 1 and which point you want to be point 2. It doesn't matter which you choose. But it is important to remember what you have chosen so you don't mix up the formula.

point 1 = (2, 1)

point 2 = (6, 4)

Step 2. Put the coordinates in the two ordered pairs into the formula for slope.

$$m = \frac{(y2 - y1)}{(x2 - x1)} = \frac{4 - 1}{6 - 2} = \frac{3}{4}$$

The slope of the line is $\frac{3}{4}$. This means that for every 3 units the line moves across, it moves 4 units up.

THINK ABOUT IT

Prove to yourself that it doesn't matter which point you call point 1 and which point you call point 2. Try doing the problem above again. This time call (6, 4) point 1 and (2, 1) point 2. Is the slope the same?

■ PRACTICE 38: The Formula for Finding Slope

Use the formula for finding slope to find the slope for each example below. Write each answer on the line.

1. point 1 = (1, 2)

   point 2 = (3, 4)

   $m=$ _____

2. point 1 = (7, 2)

   point 2 = (2, 1)

   $m=$ _____

Positive and Negative Slope

Slope can be positive or negative. If a line moves up as it goes from left to right across the page, it has a positive slope. If a line moves down as it goes from left to right across the page, it has a negative slope. Line A in the diagram below has a positive slope. Line B in the diagram below has a negative slope.

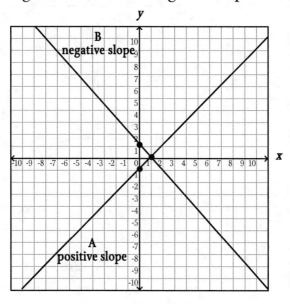

To find the slope of line A, we could take (3, 2) and (5, 4) as points on the line.

$$m = \frac{4-2}{5-3} = \frac{2}{2}$$

$$m = 1$$

The slope of line A is positive. To find the slope of line B, we could take (1, 0) and (0, 1) as points on the line.

$$m = \frac{1-0}{0-1} = \frac{1}{-1} = -1$$

The slope of line B is negative.

TIP

To remember which is positive slope and which is negative slope, picture an arrow at the right-hand end of the line. That way, an arrow pointing up will mean positive slope. An arrow pointing down will mean negative slope. For example, look below at the diagram from the previous page. Notice the arrows at the end of each line.

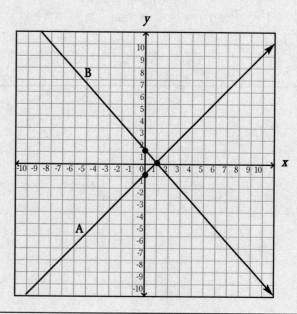

■ PRACTICE 39: Positive and Negative Slope

Decide whether the slope of the line in each example below is positive or negative. Write "positive" or "negative" on the line next to each diagram.

1.

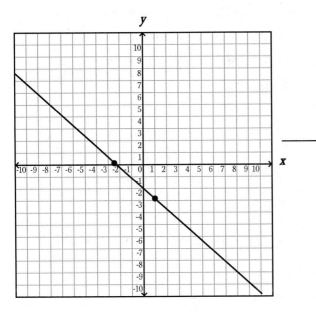

_____

2.

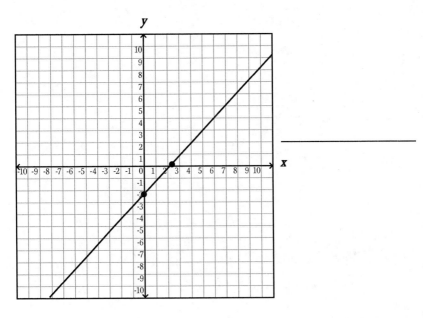

_____

Graphing a Line When You Know the Slope and One Point

The slope of a line tells you how many units the line moves up the *y*-axis as it moves across the *x*-axis. Therefore, you can use the slope of a line to help you graph the line on a coordinate plane. All you need to know is the line's slope and the coordinates of one point on the line. You then use this information to find the coordinates for a second point on the line. Once you have two points, you can draw the line.

Example 1

For example, say you know that one point on a line has the coordinates (0, −4) and that the line's slope is $m = 8$. To graph this line, follow the steps below and on the next page.

Step 1. Graph the point (0, −4) on a coordinate plane.

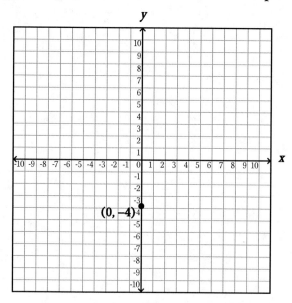

Step 2. The slope is a whole number. Make it into an improper fraction by placing it over 1.

$$m = \frac{8}{1}$$

Step 3. Find the *x*-coordinate for the second point on the line. To do this, take the denominator (the bottom number) of the fraction for the slope. Add it to the *x*-coordinate of the point you graphed in Step 1.

$$x = 0 + 1 = 1$$

Now find the *y*-coordinate for the second point in the line. To do this, take the numerator (the top number) of the fraction for the slope. Add it to the *y*-coordinate of the point you graphed in Step 1.

$$y = -4 + 8 = 4$$

The coordinates for the second point on the line are (1, 4).

Step 4. Graph the second point. Draw a straight line through the two points.

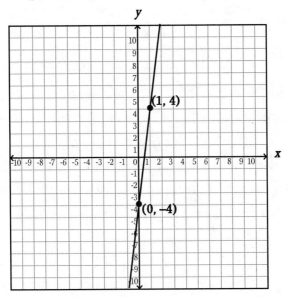

Use the same steps even if the slope is negative or a fraction (or both).

Example 2

For example, say you want to graph a line that has the point $(-4, 2)$ and the slope $m = -\dfrac{1}{2}$. To do this, follow the steps below and on the next page.

Step 1. Graph the point $(-4, 2)$ on a coordinate plane.

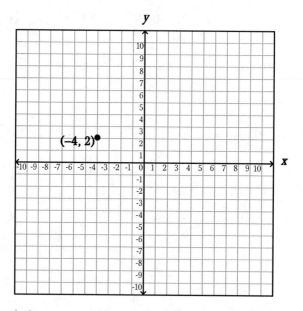

Step 2. Find the *x*-coordinate of the second point. Add the denominator of the fraction for the slope to the *x*-coordinate of the point you graphed in Step 1. Find the *y*-coordinate of the second point. Add the numerator of the fraction for the slope to the *y*-coordinate of the point you graphed in Step 1.

$$x = -4 + 2 = -2$$

$$y = 2 + -1 = 1$$

$$(-2, 1)$$

Step 3. Graph the second point. Draw a straight line through the two points.

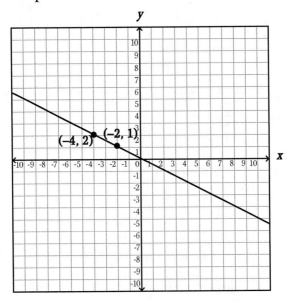

■ PRACTICE 40: Graphing a Line When You Know the Slope and One Point

The problem below gives the coordinates of one point plus the slope of a line. Use this information to graph the line.

1. $(1, 1)$; $m = 2$

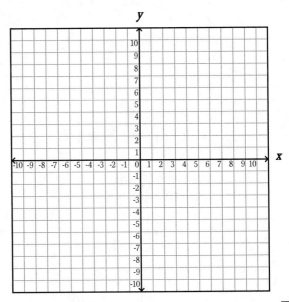

UNIT 3 REVIEW

Circle the correct answer for each question below.

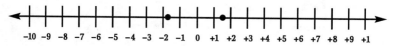

1. What numbers are graphed on the number line above?

   a. $+\dfrac{1}{2}, -1\dfrac{3}{4}$ b. $+1\dfrac{1}{2}, -2\dfrac{3}{4}$

   c. $+1\dfrac{1}{2}, -1\dfrac{3}{4}$ d. $+2\dfrac{1}{2}, -2\dfrac{1}{4}$

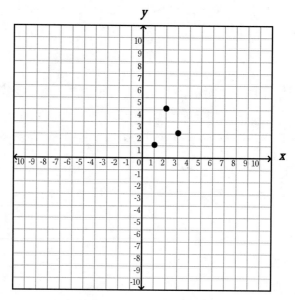

2. What points are graphed on the coordinate plane above?

   a. $(1, 1), (2, 3), (4, 2)$

   b. $(1, 1), (3, 2), (2, 4)$

   c. $(1, 1), (3, 3), (4, 2)$

   d. $(0, 1), (3, 2), (2, 4)$

3. If $x = 1$ in the equation below, what does y equal?

$$3x + 2y = 11$$

   a. 2   **b.** 3

   c. 4   **d.** 6

4. If $y = 0$ in the equation below, what does x equal?

$$4x + 2y = 8$$

   a. −1   **b.** −2

   c. 1   **d.** 2

5. Which line on the graph below represents the equation?

$$-x + 2y = 4$$

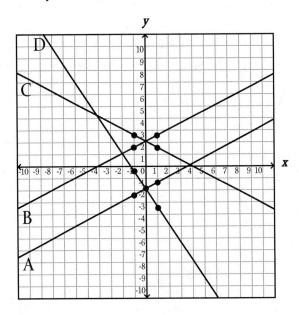

   a. line A   **b.** line B

   c. line C   **d.** line D

6. Which line below has a slope of $-\dfrac{1}{2}$?

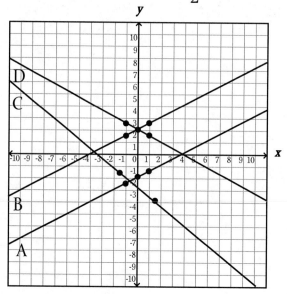

   a. line A   **b.** line B

   c. line C   **d.** line D

7. What is the slope of a line that has a point with the coordinates (3, 2) and a point with the coordinates (–4, 5)?

   a. $2\dfrac{1}{3}$

   b. $-2\dfrac{1}{3}$

   c. $\dfrac{3}{7}$

   d. $-\dfrac{3}{7}$

8. Which line below has a positive slope?

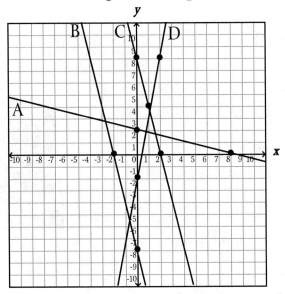

   a. line A   **b.** line B

   c. line C   **d.** line D

UNIT 3 APPLICATION ACTIVITY
Coordinates and Maps

Knowing how to use coordinates will help you find things on a map. Find a globe or a map of the United States that shows the lines of latitude and longitude. Use it to find the places listed below and on the next page. They are all national parks. On the line after each place, write its nearest coordinates. For example, the coordinates of Salt Lake City, Utah, are latitude 40° north, longitude 112° west. This is written 40° N, 112° W.

1. Sequoia National Park (California)

_____

2. Zion National Park (Utah)

_____

3. Great Smoky Mountains National Park (Tennessee)

_____

4. Hawaii Volcanoes National Park

_____

5. The Grand Canyon (Arizona)

_____

6. Acadia National Park (Maine)

_____

7. Joshua Tree National Park (California)

_____

8. Theodore Roosevelt National Park (North Dakota)

_____

9. Big Bend National Park (Texas)

_____

10. Olympic National Park (Washington)

_____

- **Optional Activity:** Find a map of your local area. On this map, find locations with which you're familiar. On a separate sheet of paper, list the locations and record the coordinates of those locations. Challenge classmates to use the coordinates to find your listed locations.

UNIT 4

Polynomial Operations

LESSON 10: Adding and Subtracting Algebraic Expressions

 GOAL: To learn how to add, subtract, and order polynomial expressions

WORDS TO KNOW

binomial	polynomial
monomial	power
operation	trinomial
ordering polynomials	

Adding and Subtracting Like Terms

You know how to solve an equation with one variable. In this lesson, you will learn how to solve equations with two or more different variables.

Let's start by reviewing terms. As you know, a term can be a number.

$$2 \qquad 736 \qquad 29 \qquad 14$$

It can be an unknown number, shown by a variable.

$$x \qquad a \qquad b$$

A term can be a constant combined with one or more variables.

$$3y \qquad \frac{1}{2}x \qquad 2mn$$

Terms can also have exponents, showing that a variable has been multiplied by itself.

$$2b^2 \qquad 14r^2s \qquad 3x^3y^3$$

These terms look much more complex than terms with just one variable and no exponents. But the rules that apply to simple terms apply to these terms, too. If terms have the same variables and the same exponents, they are like terms. You can add and subtract like terms.

Example 1

$$5rs^2 \qquad 9rs^2 \qquad 8rs^2$$

These three terms are like terms. They all have the same variables, r and s. The s in each term has the same exponent, 2, showing that it is squared. You can add these terms.

$$5rs^2 + 9rs^2 + 8rs^2 = 22rs^2$$

Example 2

$$3x^2y \qquad 5x^2y \qquad -2x^2y \qquad 8x^2y$$

These terms are like terms. They have the same variables, x and y. The x in each term has the same exponent, 2, showing that it is squared. You can add these terms. Just remember to look at the sign on each term.

$$3x^2y + 5x^2y + (-2x^2y) + 8x^2y = 14x^2y$$

Example 3

$$9xy \qquad 5f^3 \qquad -13f^2$$

These are not like terms. They do not all have the same variables. The two terms that do have the same variable—f—have different exponents. These terms cannot be added or subtracted.

You can use coefficients as an easy way to add or subtract like terms. Coefficients are the constants in terms—the numbers that multiply the variables. For example, in the term $3x$, 3 is the coefficient. Even if no constant is written beside the variable— for example, in the term x—the term has a coefficient. The term x could be written as $1x$. The coefficient of x is 1. To add or subtract like terms, just add and subtract the coefficients. For example, look at the problem $7y - y + 9y$. You could simplify this to $(7 - 1 + 9) y = 15y$. Just remember to use 1 as the coefficient for a variable with no constant.

■ PRACTICE 41: Adding and Subtracting Like Terms

Look at each pair of terms below. Write L if the terms are like terms. Write U if the terms are unlike terms. Write each answer on the line.

1. $5y, 8u$ _____

2. $8xy, 16xy$ _____

3. $23pq, 35pq^2$ _____

4. $5dt, 7d^3t$ _____

5. $3m^2b^2c^2, 19m^2b^2c^2$ _____

6. $56q, 35q^2$ _____

7. $25r^2s^3, 59r^3s^2$ _____

8. $9w^3v^4, 18w^3v^4$ _____

Add or subtract the like terms below. Write each answer on the line.

9. $5y - 8y =$ _____

10. $8xy + 16xy =$ _____

11. $-23pq^2 + 35pq^2 =$ _____

12. $5dt - 7dt =$ _____

13. $-4cd - 2cd - 7cd + 5cd =$ _____

14. $3m^2b^2c^2 + 19m^2b^2c^2 =$ _____

15. $30p - 2p - 20p + 10p =$ _____

16. $25r^3s^2 - 59r^3s^2 =$ _____

17. $-5ef^2g + 6ef^2g =$ _____

18. $6m + 8m + 11m + 14m =$ _____

Ordering Polynomials

"Poly" means "many." An expression with one or more terms is called a **polynomial.** The terms are separated by a plus or a minus sign. Polynomials are formed by adding, subtracting, or multiplying numbers and variables. These are all examples of polynomials:

$$x^2 \qquad 3x^3 + 4y \qquad 42m - 13 \qquad 73y^3 + 3y^2 - 6y + 8$$

Some of these polynomials have several terms with the same variable. However, the variable in each term has a different exponent. Here is another example of a polynomial where the same variable has different exponents:

$$x^3 + x^2$$

The term x^3 stands for $(x)\,(x)\,(x)$. We say that x^3 has a **power** of 3. The term x^2 stands for $(x)\,(x)$. We say that x^2 has a power of 2. Both these terms have the same variable. But they have different exponents, or powers. When a polynomial has different powers for the same variable, write the terms so the powers are in decreasing order. For example, $6y + 3y^3 + 2y^2 - 1$ should be written so that the variable with the highest power comes first.

$$3y^3 + 2y^2 + 6y - 1$$

Notice that y^3 comes first, then y^2, and then y. (The variable y is actually y^1. $y = y^1$. Because y^1 and y mean the same thing, we save time by just writing the variable without the exponent.) Whole numbers by themselves, such as -1, are put at the end of the polynomial.

Look at the following example.

Example 1

$$3d + 7 - 6d^3 + 4d^2$$

This polynomial is not in order. It should be written to look like this:

$$-6d^3 + 4d^2 + 3d + 7$$

When you arrange terms in a polynomial, don't forget about positive and negative signs. Keep the sign for each term with the term it belongs to.

The word *mono* means "one." A polynomial with just one term is called a **monomial.** These are all examples of monomials:

$$2 \quad -3x \quad 8x^2y \quad -5x^2y^3z$$

The word *bi* means "two." A polynomial with two terms is called a **binomial.** These are all examples of binomials:

$$3w + 2 \quad c - 9d \quad 4x^2 - 1$$

The word *tri* means "three." A polynomial with three terms is called a **trinomial.** These are all examples of trinomials:

$$9x^2 + 17ab + 73z^2 \quad b^2 + 4b + 1 \quad 5x^2 + 4x - 9$$

■ PRACTICE 42: Ordering Polynomials

Write the following polynomials so that they are in order. Write your answer on the line after each polynomial.

Example: $2 + 3x + 3x^2$ $\qquad$ $3x^2 + 3x + 2$

1. $-5 - 6y + 9y^3$

_____

2. $-45m^3 + 9m^2 - 5m + 12 + 6m^8$

_____

3. $8g^3 - 100 + g$

_____

4. $5m^3 - 23m^2 + 6m - 90 + m^4$

_____

Adding and Subtracting Polynomials

To add or subtract two polynomials, arrange the like terms in columns.

Example 1

To add $4x + 6y$ and $2y + 7x$, arrange the like terms under each other. Then add, column by column.

$$\begin{array}{r} 4x + 6y \\ 7x + 2y \\ \hline 11x + 8y \end{array}$$

The answer is $11x + 8y$ because $4x + 7x = 11x$ and $6y + 2y = 8y$.

Example 2

Let's add two more polynomials. To add $4c + 2d$ and $-10c - 4d$, arrange the like terms under each other. Then add, column by column.

$$\begin{array}{r} 4c + 2d \\ -10c - 4d \\ \hline -6c - 2d \end{array}$$

The answer is $-6c - 2d$.

Before you add or subtract polynomials, you should simplify them. To do this, add like terms. The easiest way to simplify a long polynomial is to put like terms in parentheses. Then add or subtract the like terms in each set of parentheses.

Example 3

$$12 - 7t + 8 + 12t - 6 + 14t$$

Step 1. First, put all the t terms together. Put parentheses around the group of like terms. Then do the same for the constant terms.

$$(-7t + 12t + 14t) + (12 + 8 - 6)$$

Step 2. Next, add all the terms in each set of parentheses. Take away the parentheses when you're finished adding.

$$19t + 14$$

Look at another example.

Example 4

$$4m + 6 + 7m^2 - 3y - y + 5 + m^2 + 1 - 3m^2 + 4y - m$$

Step 1. Put the like terms into parentheses.

$$(4m - m) + (7m^2 + m^2 - 3m^2) + (-3y - y + 4y) + (6 + 5 + 1)$$

Count the terms to make sure you didn't forget any. The m^2 terms were all put into one set of parentheses. The m terms were put into another set of parentheses, and so on.

Step 2. Now, add each group of like terms.

$$3m + 5m^2 + 12$$

Notice that the y terms cancelled themselves out:
$$-3y - y + 4y = 0$$

Step 3. Now arrange the terms if they are not in correct order.

$$5m^2 + 3m + 12$$

Example 5

Now let's try to add two polynomials. Look at the example below.

$$(r^2 + 4f^2 + 8r^2) + (13r^2 + 5f^2 + 7f^2)$$

Step 1. Before you add these two polynomials, simplify them. Start with the first one.

$$(r^2 + 8r^2) + 4f^2$$

$$9r^2 + 4f^2$$

Step 2. Now simplify the second polynomial.

$$13r^2 + (5f^2 + 7f^2)$$

$$13r^2 + 12f^2$$

Step 3. Now you have two simplified polynomials. To add these polynomials, stack them so that the like terms are in the same column.

$$9r^2 + \ 4f^2$$

$$13r^2 + 12f^2$$

Step 4. Now, add each column. $9r^2$ plus $13r^2$ equals $22r^2$. $4f^2 + 12f^2$ equals $16f^2$.

$$9r^2 + \ 4f^2$$
$$\underline{13r^2 + 12f^2}$$
$$22r^2 + 16f^2$$

The new polynomial is $22r^2 + 16f^2$.

You have learned to add a polynomial to another polynomial. Do you think you can add a monomial to a polynomial? Try adding the polynomial $6x^2 + xy + 3ab$ to the monomial $4ab$. Write your answer on a separate sheet of paper.

■ PRACTICE 43: Adding and Subtracting Polynomials

Combine like terms to simplify each polynomial below. Write each new polynomial on the line.

1. $m^3 - 17 + 23 - m^3$ _____

2. $2x - 7y^2 - 12y^2 + 17y^2 - 8$ _____

3. $14 - 4k - 7k^2 + 16k - 12k^2 + 13k$ _____

Add the following polynomials. Write each answer on the line.

Example:

$6e + 3m + 10s$ and $-3e - 2m - 6s + 2f$

$$
\begin{array}{r}
6e + 3m + 10s \\
-3e - 2m - 6s + 2f \\
\hline
3e + m + 4s + 2f
\end{array}
$$

4. $3x^3 + 4x^2$ and $-12x^3 - 7x^2 - 7x =$

_____

5. $-r^2 + 4t^2 + 8s^2$ and $13r^2 + 5s^2 - 7t^2 =$

_____

6. $20 - 3x + 4y$ and $-5x - 7y + 10 =$

_____

Simplify each polynomial below. Then add each pair of polynomials together. Write the new polynomial on the line.

Example:

$2s^2 - 17s^2 + 23r^2 - r^2$ and $7s^2 + 6r^2 - 3s^2 + 12r^2$

$(2s^2 - 17s^2) + (23r^2 - r^2)$ and $(7s^2 - 3s^2) + (6r^2 + 12r^2)$

$-15s^2 + 22r^2$ and $4s^2 + 18r^2$

$$\begin{array}{r} -15s^2 + 22r^2 \\ +4s^2 + 18r^2 \\ \hline -11s^2 + 40r^2 \end{array}$$

7. $7m^2 + 4n^2 + 15n^2 - 5m^2$ and $2n^2 - 8n^2 + 12m^2 + 8m^2 =$

_____

8. $8cd^2 + 20c^2 - 12cd^2 - 14c^2$ and $5c^2 + 3cd^2 - 9cd^2 + 6c^2 =$

_____

9. $5b^2 - 4m^2 + 10b^2 + 19m^2$ and $7m^2 - 12b^2 + 3b^2 - 9m^2 =$

_____

LESSON 11: Multiplying and Dividing Algebraic Expressions

 GOAL: To learn how to multiply and divide variables with exponents, monomials, binomials, and polynomials

WORDS TO KNOW

difference	product
FOIL method	special binomials

Multiplying Variables with Exponents

It is important to learn how to work with exponents. As you know, exponents are the small, raised numbers that show how many times a number is multiplied by itself.

Example 1

In the multiplication problem $(x^2)(x^4)$, the variable in both terms is x. The exponents are 2 and 4. The exponents tell you how many times x is multiplied by itself.

$$x^2 = x \bullet x$$

$$x^4 = x \bullet x \bullet x \bullet x$$

Therefore:

$$(x^2) \bullet (x^4) = ?$$

$$(x \bullet x) \bullet (x \bullet x \bullet x \bullet x) = ?$$

$$(x \bullet x \bullet x \bullet x \bullet x \bullet x) = x^6$$

The **product** (the result of multiplication) of x^2 times x^4 is x^6. To find the exponent of the product, you just add the exponents of the terms: $2 + 4 = 6$.

Now look at another problem.

Example 2

$$(z^5)(z^3) = ?$$

In this problem, both terms have the variable z. The exponents are 5 and 3.

$$(z^5)(z^3) = (z \bullet z \bullet z \bullet z \bullet z)(z \bullet z \bullet z) = ?$$

$$(z \bullet z \bullet z \bullet z \bullet z \bullet z \bullet z \bullet z) = z^8$$

The product of z^5 times z^3 is z^8. You can add the exponents of the terms to find the exponent of the product: $5 + 3 = 8$.

Multiplying Two Terms with the Same Variable

To multiply two terms using the same variable, add the exponents.

Here are some examples of this rule.

$$(s^2)(s^3) = s^{2+3} = s^5$$

$$(m^2)(m) = m^{2+1} = m^3$$

$$(j^5)(j^4) = j^{5+4} = j^9$$

 TIP

Sometimes you will see the symbol "$\bullet$", as in $x \bullet x = 16$. This is another symbol for multiplication. $x \bullet x = 16$ means that "x times x equals 16." Try to remember this symbol so that you will know it when you see it!

■ PRACTICE 44: Multiplying Variables with Exponents

Use the rule for exponents to solve the problems below. Write each answer on the line.

Example: $(s)(s^2) = s^3$ $\qquad$ $(s) \bullet (s \bullet s) = s^{1+2} = s^3$

1. $(d^2)(d^4) =$ _____

2. $(n)(n^3)(n^5) =$ _____

3. $(s^3)(s)(s^4) =$ _____

4. $(t)(t) =$ _____

5. $(d^8)(d^9) =$ _____

6. $(y^3)(y)(y^2)(y^6) =$ _____

7. $(m^4)(m)(m^2)(m^5) =$ _____

8. $(q^7)(q^8)(q^3) =$ _____

Multiplying Monomials

You already know how to add and subtract monomials, or polynomials with one term. Now you will learn how to multiply them.

> ### Multiplying Monomials with the Same Variable
> To multiply monomials that have the same variable, add the exponents of the variables.

Look at the following example.

Example 1

$$(7v^2) \cdot (3v^3) = ?$$

Step 1. Multiply the coefficients of each monomial.

$$7(3) = 21$$

Step 2. Multiply the variables by adding their exponents.

$$v^2 \cdot v^3 = v^5$$

Step 3. Multiply the answers of the first two steps to get the final answer.

$$(21)(v^5) = 21v^5$$

The answer is $21v^5$.

Try another example.

Example 2

$$(5r^4) \cdot (-7r^5) = ?$$

Step 1. Multiply the coefficients.

$$(5)(-7) = -35$$

Step 2. Multiply the variables by adding their exponents.

$$(r^4)(r^5) = r^9$$

Step 3. Multiply the results of the first two steps.

$$(-35)(r^9) = -35r^9$$

The answer is $-35r^9$.

■ PRACTICE 45: Multiplying Monomials

Multiply the following monomials. Write each answer on the line.

Example: $(2m^2)(-8m^3) = -16m^5$

1. $(6c^8)(4c^4) = $ _____

2. $(3f^2)(9f^9) = $ _____

3. $(-3t^4)(-7t^7) = $ _____

4. $(3c^6)(-9c^9) = $ _____

5. $(4b)(9b^5) = $ _____

6. $(6y)(-2y) = $ _____

7. $(8h^3)(9h^7) = $ _____

8. $(-2t^6)(-8t^8) = $ _____

Dividing Variables with Exponents

You have learned how to add, subtract, and multiply monomials. Now you will learn how to divide monomials.

You learned that when you multiply monomials with the same variable, you add the exponents. Now here is a rule for dividing monomials.

Dividing Monomials with the Same Variable

To divide monomials that have the same variable, subtract the exponents of the variables.

Look at the example below.

Example 1

$$\frac{z^4}{z^2} = \frac{z \bullet z \bullet z \bullet z}{z \bullet z}$$

To divide z^4 by z^2, cancel two z's from the numerator and two z's from the denominator.

$$\frac{\cancel{z} \bullet \cancel{z} \bullet z \bullet z}{\cancel{z} \bullet \cancel{z}}$$

Look at what you have left: $(z \bullet z)$ or z^2. This is the same answer you would get if you subtracted the exponent of the denominator (2) from the exponent of the numerator (4): $4 - 2 = 2$.

Look at another example.

Example 2

$$\frac{m^6}{m^3}$$

If you write out these exponents, you get:

$$\frac{m \bullet m \bullet m \bullet m \bullet m \bullet m}{m \bullet m \bullet m}$$

Cancel out three m's from both the numerator and the denominator.

$$\frac{\cancel{m} \bullet \cancel{m} \bullet \cancel{m} \bullet m \bullet m \bullet m}{\cancel{m} \bullet \cancel{m} \bullet \cancel{m}}$$

Look at what you have left: $(m \bullet m \bullet m)$ or m^3. The exponent of the answer is the **difference** between the exponent of the numerator and the exponent of the denominator: $6 - 3 = 3$.

Look at the examples below. These are all division problems. They show you that you can divide monomials with exponents by subtracting the exponent of the denominator from the exponent of the numerator.

$$\frac{r^7}{r^4} = r^{7-4} = r^3$$

$$\frac{j^5}{j^4} = j^{5-4} = j$$

$$\frac{w^{10}}{w^4} = w^{10-4} = w^6$$

$$\frac{c^4}{c} = c^{4-1} = c^3$$

■ PRACTICE 46: Dividing Variables with Exponents

Solve each division problem below. Write each answer on the line.

Example: $\dfrac{q^4}{q^2} = q^{4-2} = q^2$

1. $\dfrac{x^{17}}{x^8} =$ _____

2. $\dfrac{v^3}{v^2} =$ _____

3. $\dfrac{b^7}{b^3} =$ _____

4. $\dfrac{r^{10}}{r^2} =$ _____

5. $\dfrac{d^9}{d^2} =$ _____

6. $\dfrac{k^5}{k^4} =$ _____

7. $\dfrac{n^6}{n} =$ _____

8. $\dfrac{m^{13}}{m^6} =$ _____

9. $\dfrac{h^{12}}{h^8} =$ _____

10. $\dfrac{s^5}{s^4} =$ _____

THINK ABOUT IT

You just learned that you can "cancel out" like variables in the numerator and denominator of a fraction. Why do you think this works? Write your answer on a separate sheet of paper.

Dividing Monomials

You have learned to divide monomials with exponents. Now you will learn to divide monomials with coefficients and exponents.

Read the rule below.

Dividing Monomials

To divide one monomial by another monomial:

1. Divide the coefficients.
2. Subtract the exponents.
3. Multiply the results of steps 1 and 2.

Example 1

For instance, divide $16j^5$ by $2j^3$ following these three steps.

$$\frac{16j^5}{2j^3}$$

Step 1. Divide the coefficients of each monomial (16 and 2). 16 divided by 2 equals 8.

$$\frac{16}{2} = 8$$

Step 2. Divide the variables by subtracting the exponents. The exponent of the numerator (5) minus the exponent of the denominator (3) equals 2.

$$\frac{j^5}{j^3} = j^{(5-3)} = j^2$$

Step 3. Multiply the results of the first two steps.

$$(8)\,(j^2) = 8j^2$$

The solution is $8j^2$.

Dividing monomials is one way to simplify expressions. The monomial $8j^2$ is really just a simplified form of $\dfrac{16j^5}{2j^3}$. Monomials can be simplified if they have a common denominator, if they have the same variables, or both.

Example 2

Let's try to simplify the expression below.

$$\frac{-25m^5}{5m}$$

Step 1. Divide the coefficients.

$$\frac{-25}{5} = -5$$

Step 2. Divide the variables by subtracting the exponent of the denominator from the exponent of the numerator.

$$\frac{m^5}{m} = m^4$$

Step 3. Multiply the results of the first two steps.

$$-5(m^4) = -5m^4$$

$-5m^4$ is a simplified version of $\dfrac{-25m^5}{5m}$.

Look at the example below.

Example 3

$$\frac{16m^5}{4b^3}$$

Can this fraction be simplified by the three-step process? You can do step 1.

$$\frac{16}{4} = 4$$

Can you do step 2? The variables in the numerator and denominator are not the same, so you can't do step 2. The fraction can only be simplified by step 1.

$$\frac{4m^5}{b^3}$$

Now look at another example.

Example 4

$$\frac{15m^5}{4b^3}$$

Can you do step 1? No, 15 and 4 have no common denominator. Can you do step 2? No, the variables are not the same. This fraction cannot be simplified.

■ PRACTICE 47: Dividing Monomials

Simplify each expression. Write your answer on the line. Write "no" if the expression cannot be simplified.

Example: $\dfrac{3w^8}{15w^7} = \dfrac{w}{5}$

$$\frac{3}{15} = \frac{1}{5}$$

$$\frac{w^8}{w^7} = w$$

$$\frac{1}{5}\left(\frac{w}{1}\right) = \frac{w}{5}$$

1. $\dfrac{45r^3}{9r^2} =$ _____

2. $\dfrac{-18d^4}{-3d^4} =$ _____

3. $\dfrac{a^4}{a^3} =$ _____

4. $\dfrac{13p^4}{5q^2} =$ _____

5. $\dfrac{2m^8}{3m^2} =$ _____

6. $\dfrac{-48k^4}{6k^2} =$ _____

Multiplying a Polynomial by a Monomial

You have learned how to add polynomials. Now you will learn how to multiply polynomials by monomials.

Read the rule below.

Multiplying a Polynomial by a Monomial

To multiply a polynomial by a monomial, multiply each term of the polynomial by the monomial. Then combine terms.

Look at the example below.

Example 1

$$6(m + b)$$

Step 1. In this example, 6 is a monomial. You want to multiply it by the polynomial $m + b$. First, multiply 6 by both terms in the polynomial.

$$6(m) + 6(b)$$

Step 2. Next, combine the two terms.

$$6m + 6b$$

The solution is $6m + 6b$.

Example 2

Here's a more difficult example. Multiply the polynomial $(2x - 5y)$ by the monomial $3x$.

$$3x(2x - 5y)$$

Step 1. First, multiply both terms in the polynomial by the monomial $3x$.

$$3x(2x) - 3x(5y)$$

Step 2. Next, combine terms.

$$6x^2 - 15xy$$

Notice that $x \bullet x = x^2$, so $3x \bullet 2x = 6x^2$. Also notice that when you multiply two terms with different variables, you multiply the coefficient and keep both variables.

$$3x(5y) = 15xy$$

The answer is $6x^2 - 15xy$.

Example 3

Let's look at an example with a negative monomial. Multiply the polynomial $(6n - b^2)$ by the monomial $-3b$:

$$-3b(6n - b^2)$$

Step 1. Multiply both terms in the polynomial by the monomial $-3b$.

$$(-3b)(6n) - (-3b)(b^2)$$

Step 2. Combine terms.

$$-18bn - (-3b^3)$$

$$-18bn + 3b^3$$

Step 3. Last, put the polynomial in order.

$$3b^3 - 18bn$$

The answer is $3b^3 - 18bn$.

■ PRACTICE 48: Multiplying a Polynomial by a Monomial

Solve each multiplication problem below. Write your answer on the line after each problem. Make sure the polynomials in your answers are in order.

1. $2(m-5) =$ _____

2. $5p(6p+3q) =$ _____

3. $-5t(-6t+4s) =$ _____

4. $-5y(2x-5y) =$ _____

5. $-7x(x^2+2x^3) =$ _____

6. $-3(r+s) =$ _____

Multiplying Binomials

Binomials are polynomials that have two terms. $4x^2 - 3mn$ is a binomial. So is $x+y$. In this section, you will learn how to multiply binomials.

Multiplying binomials is simple. You just need to make sure you multiply both parts of one binomial by both parts of the other.

Look at the following example.

Example 1

$$(6x+4) \bullet (7x+3) = ?$$

Step 1. Multiply the first terms of the two binomials.

$$6x \cdot 7x = 42x^2$$

$$(6x + 4)(7x + 3) = 42x^2 \ldots$$

Step 2. Multiply the outside terms. Then add the product to the product of the first two terms.

$$6x \cdot 3 = 18x$$

$$(6x + 4)(7x + 3) = 42x^2 + 18x \ldots$$

You have now multiplied the first part of one binomial by both parts of the other binomial.

Step 3. Multiply the inside terms. Then add the product to the other two products.

$$4 \cdot 7x = 28x$$

$$(6x + 4)(7x + 3) = 42x^2 + 18x + 28x \ldots$$

Step 4. Multiply the last terms. Then add the product to the other three products.

$$4 \cdot 3 = 12$$

$$(6x + 4)(7x + 3) = 42x^2 + 18x + 28x + 12$$

You have now multiplied both terms in the first binomial by both terms in the second binomial.

Step 5. Combine the like terms. $18x$ and $28x$ are both x terms. Add them together.

$$42x^2 + (18x + 28x) + 12$$

$$42x^2 + 46x + 12$$

The FOIL Method

If you look at the first four steps, you will see an easy rule to remember:

First terms

Outside terms

Inside terms

Last terms

This is called the **FOIL method** of binomial multiplication.

Practice the FOIL method on some more problems.

Example 2

$$(5t + 6) \bullet (7t - 1) = ?$$

Step 1. Multiply the first terms in each binomial.

$$(5t + 6)(7t - 1) = 35t^2 \ldots$$

Step 2. Multiply the outside terms in each binomial. Then add the product to the product of the first terms.

$$(5t + 6)(7t - 1) = 35t^2 - 5t \ldots$$

Step 3. Multiply the inside terms. Then add this product to the other two products.

$$(5t + 6)(7t - 1) = 35t^2 - 5t + 42t \ldots$$

Step 4. Multiply the last terms in each binomial. Add this product to the other three products.

$$(5t + 6)(7t - 1) = 35t^2 - 5t + 42t - 6$$

Step 5. Finally, combine like terms and simplify.

$$(5t+6)(7t-1) = 35t^2 + (-5t+42t) - 6$$
$$= 35t^2 + 37t - 6$$

Here's another example.

Example 3

$$(2u-5) \bullet (7u+8) = ?$$

F: $(2u-5)(7u+8) = 14u^2 \ldots$

O: $(2u-5)(7u+8) = 14u^2 + 16u \ldots$

I: $(2u-5)(7u+8) = 14u^2 + 16u - 35u \ldots$

L: $(2u-5)(7u+8) = 14u^2 + 16u - 35u - 40$

Combine like terms.

$$(2u-5)(7u+8) = 14u^2 - 19u - 40$$

THINK ABOUT IT

What if you multiplied the terms in a different order? What if you used FILO instead of FOIL? Would you still get the correct answer? In the space below, try it with one of the examples you just read.

■ PRACTICE 49: Multiplying Binomials

Use the FOIL method to multiply each problem below. Write each answer on the line.

Example: $(s+5)(s+8) = s^2 + 13s + 40$

$$s^2 + 8s + 5s + 40 =$$

$$s^2 + 13s + 40$$

1. $(t+6)(3t+9) = $ _____

2. $(6m-8)(3m+2) = $ _____

3. $(g+4)(g-4) = $ _____

4. $(10x+5)(3x+2) = $ _____

Multiplying Special Binomials

Certain pairs of binomials are known as **special binomials.** These binomials each have the same variable and constant, but one binomial asks you to add and the other asks you to subtract.

Look at the example below.

Example 1

$$(y+4) \bullet (y-4)$$

These pairs of binomials are special because when you multiply them together, the two middle terms cancel each other out.

Use the FOIL method to multiply the two binomials.

$$(y+4)(y-4) = y^2 + 4y - 4y - 16$$

Collect the like terms.

$$y^2 - 16$$

Notice that the $+4y$ and $-4y$ cancel each other out when you collect like terms.

The product of any two special binomials is always the variable squared minus the constant squared ($y^2 - 16$).

Let's try another example.

Example 2

$$(c + d) \bullet (c - d) = ?$$

$$(c + d)(c - d) = c^2 - cd + cd - d^2$$

Collect like terms.

$$(c + d)(c - d) = c^2 - d^2$$

Multiplying Special Binomials
Any time you need to multiply two binomials with the form $(x + y)$ times $(x - y)$, use this rule:
$$(x + y) \bullet (x - y) = x^2 - (y^2)$$

Example 3

Let's try some examples to show you that this rule is true.

$$(n + 8) \bullet (n - 8) = ?$$

Step 1. Use the FOIL method to multiply the terms in the binomials.

$$(n + 8)(n - 8) = n^2 - 8n + 8n - 64$$

Step 2. Combine like terms. The *n* terms will cancel each other out.

$$(n+8)(n-8) = n^2 - 64$$

The answer is $n^2 - 64$. This is the same as $n^2 - (8^2)$.

Let's try another example.

Example 4

$$(3x+6) \bullet (3x-6) = ?$$

Step 1. Use the FOIL method to multiply the terms in the two binomials.

$$(3x+6)(3x-6) = 9x^2 - 18x + 18x - 36$$

Step 2. Collect like terms. The *x* terms will cancel each other out.

$$9x^2 - 36$$

The answer is $9x^2 - 36$. This is the same as $3x^2 - (6^2)$.

■ PRACTICE 50: Multiplying Special Binomials

Multiply the following special binomials. Write each answer on the line.

1. $(w+2) \bullet (w-2) = $ _____

2. $(y+3x) \bullet (y-3x) = $ _____

3. $(r+m) \bullet (r-m) = $ _____

4. $(9e+9f) \bullet (9e-9f) = $ _____

LESSON 12: Factoring

> **GOAL:** To learn how to factor binomial, trinomial, and polynomial expressions

WORDS TO KNOW

common factor	factoring
complete factoring	greatest common factor (GCF)
difference between two squares	property
factor	single term

What Is Factoring?

You know that the result of multiplying is called the product. If you multiply 2 times 3, the product is 6. But what do you call 2 and 3? They are called factors of 6. A **factor** is a number that is multiplied by another number to get a product.

When you break a term into its factors, you are **factoring** the term. For instance, the product of 5 and 4 is 20. This means that 20 can be broken up and written as the product of 5 and 4.

$$20 = 5 \bullet 4$$

The numbers 5 and 4 are factors of 20.

Factoring is not dividing. In division, you are given the product and one factor and told to find the other factor. With division, there is only one possible answer. In factoring, there is more than one possible answer. Above, you factored 20 into 5 and 4. You could also factor 20 into 10 and 2, or 20 and 1.

$$20 = 10 \bullet 2$$

$$20 = 20 \bullet 1$$

Negative numbers can also be factors. For example, –10 and –2, –5 and –4, or –20 and –1 are also factors of 20.

$$20 = -5 \bullet -4$$

$$20 = -10 \bullet -2$$

$$20 = -20 \bullet -1$$

Factoring

Any numbers that, when multiplied, equal a certain product can be used as factors of that product.

Remember, when you multiply two negative numbers, your answer is a positive number. When you multiply a negative and a positive number, your answer is a negative number.

A term or an expression can be the product of more than two factors. The monomial term $4y$ can be factored in at least seven different ways.

$$4y = 4 \bullet y$$

$$4y = 2 \bullet 2y$$

$$4y = 2 \bullet 2 \bullet y$$

$$4y = (-4) \bullet (-y)$$

$$4y = (-2) \bullet (-2y)$$

$$4y = (-2) \bullet (-2) \bullet y$$

$$4y = (-2) \bullet 2 \bullet (-y)$$

The term $9m^3$ can also be factored in many ways.

$9m^3 = 9 \cdot m^3$

$9m^3 = 9 \cdot m^2 \cdot m$

$9m^3 = 9 \cdot m \cdot m \cdot m$

$9m^3 = 3 \cdot 3 \cdot m^3$

$9m^3 = 3 \cdot 3 \cdot m^2 \cdot m$

$9m^3 = 3 \cdot 3 \cdot m \cdot m \cdot m$

$9m^3 = (-9) \cdot (-m^3)$

$9m^3 = 9 \cdot (-m^2) \cdot (-m)$

$9m^3 = (-9) \cdot (-m) \cdot m \cdot m$

$9m^3 = 9 \cdot (-m) \cdot (-m) \cdot m$

$9m^3 = (-3) \cdot (-3) \cdot m^3$

$9m^3 = (-3) \cdot 3 \cdot (-m^3)$

$9m^3 = (-3) \cdot (-3) \cdot m^2 \cdot m$

$9m^3 = (-3) \cdot (-3) \cdot m \cdot m \cdot m$

$9m^3 = (-3) \cdot 3 \cdot m^2 \cdot (-m)$

Factoring is useful because it lets you look at a **single term** in an equation in different ways. This may help you reach a solution.

Knowing how to factor is useful when you need to find the dimensions of something. Susan is planning to put a fence around her garden. She knows that its area is 40 square feet, and that this area is the length of the garden times its width ($A = lw$). Now she needs to know the garden's perimeter (the distance around the garden). She realizes that if she factors the number 40 she can find the garden's length and width. Susan knows that she can factor the number 40 many ways. Since she can see that the garden is a little more than twice as long as it is wide, she decides to use the factors 4 • 10. Now she can use the formula for finding the perimeter of a 4-sided shape: p (perimeter) $= 2l$ (length) $+ 2w$ (width).

$p = 2(10) + 2(4)$

$p = 28$ feet

Susan now knows that she needs to buy 28 feet of fencing. Because she knows how to factor, she didn't have to measure anything!

■ PRACTICE 51: Finding Factors

Factor each number or term at least three ways. Write your answers on the three lines after each problem.

Example: $18x^3 = 18 \cdot x^2 \cdot x$

$18 \cdot x \cdot x \cdot x$

$9 \cdot 2 \cdot x^3$

1. $7s^2 = $ _____

_____

_____

2. $9r = $ _____

_____

_____

3. $3xy = $ _____

_____

_____

4. $21t^2 = $ _____

_____

_____

Finding the Greatest Common Factor

You factor a number by breaking it up into parts. You can also factor a polynomial by breaking it up into parts. These parts will include numbers, monomials, and other polynomials.

To factor a polynomial, first look for a term that is common to every term in the polynomial. This means a term that is a part of each term in the polynomial. For instance, look at the polynomial $5a + 2ab + a^2$. The term a is a common term, because there is an a in each term in the polynomial.

A common term can also be a number that can be divided into each term in the polynomial. Look at the polynomial

$5m + 25k + 15n$. The number 5 is a common term because each number in the polynomial can be divided by 5. A term that is common to all the terms in a polynomial is called the **common factor**.

Example 1

Look at the binomial $2m + 4n$.

Step 1. Find a common factor for all the terms. Both terms can be divided by 2. Use 2 as the common factor.

Step 2. Divide the polynomial by the common factor.

$$\frac{2m + 4n}{2}$$

Step 3. To solve this division problem, divide each term by 2. $2m$ divided by 2 equals m. $4n$ divided by 2 equals $2n$.

$$\frac{2m}{2} = m \qquad\qquad \frac{4n}{2} = 2n$$

Step 4. Add the two results.

$$m + 2n$$

Step 5. You now know the two factors of the original equation. One factor is the common factor (2). The other factor is the result of your division problem ($m + 2n$). So the binomial $2m + 4n$ can be broken down into $(2) \cdot (m + 2n)$. If you multiplied these two factors, you would get the original equation.

$$2(m + 2n) = 2m + 4n$$

Now look at another problem.

Example 2

$$6j^2 - 24j$$

Step 1. Find the common factor. What term can both $6j^2$ and $-24j$ be divided by? $2j$, $3j$, and $6j$ are all factors of both $6j^2$ and $-24j$. However, you should always look for the **greatest common factor.** This is the largest possible term that will divide evenly into each term of the polynomial. In this case, the greatest common factor is $6j$. $6j$ is larger than either $2j$ or $3j$.

Step 2. Divide the binomial by $6j$ by dividing each term by $6j$.

$$\frac{6j^2 - 24j}{6j}$$

$$\frac{6j^2}{6j} = j \qquad \frac{-24j}{6j} = -4$$

Step 3. Add the two results.

$$j + (-4) = j - 4$$

The factors of $6j^2 - 24j$ are $(6j)$ and $(j-4)$.

Here is one last example.

Example 3

$$4w^3 + 8w^2 - 12w$$

Step 1. Find the greatest common factor. All four terms can be divided by $4w$.

Step 2. Divide the polynomial by $4w$ by dividing each term by $4w$.

$$\frac{4w^3 + 8w^2 - 12w}{4w}$$

$$\frac{4w^3}{4w} = w^2 \qquad \frac{8w^2}{4w} = 2w \qquad \frac{-12w}{4w} = -3$$

Step 3. Add the results.

$$w^2 + 2w - 3$$

The factors of $4w^3 + 8w^2 - 12w$ are $(4w)$ and $(w^2 + 2w - 3)$.

THINK ABOUT IT

Sometimes, the greatest common factor in a polynomial turns out to be the smallest coefficient in the polynomial. When you look for the greatest common factor, first find the smallest coefficient in the polynomial. See if this number divides evenly into all other terms in the polynomial. Why do you think you should look for the smallest coefficient to find the greatest common factor?

■ PRACTICE 52: Finding the Greatest Common Factor

Factor each polynomial below and on the next page. Use the greatest common factor.

Example: $8u + 8 = 8 \bullet (u + 1)$

$$\frac{8u + 8}{8} = \frac{8u}{8} + \frac{8}{8} = u + 1$$

1. $12h - 24 = $ _____

2. $7q^2 + 49q = $ _____

3. $bc - bm =$ _____

4. $16h^3 + 24h^2 - 40h =$ _____

5. $n^3m^2 - n^2m =$ _____

6. $300 - 1200g =$ _____

The Difference Between Two Squares

You have already learned that if you multiply the sum of two terms $(x + y)$ by the difference of the same two terms $(x - y)$, the answer will be the square of the first term minus the square of the second term, or $x^2 - y^2$.

$$(x + y) \bullet (x - y) = (x^2 - y^2)$$

Now you will learn how to factor expressions such as $x^2 - y^2$.

Look at the example below. Notice that the two binomials are being multiplied. The product is the square of the first term in both binomials (y^2) minus the square of the second term in both binomials (-16).

$$(y + 4)(y - 4) = y^2 - 4y + 4y - 16$$
$$y^2 - 16$$

When factoring, you can use the opposite of this rule to help you! Remember this when you need to factor any expression that is the square of one term minus the square of another term. This type of expression is called the **difference between two squares.**

Example 1

For example, look at the binomial $y^2 - 16$. y^2 is the square of y.

And 16 is the square of 4. One square is being subtracted from another square.

Example 2

Here is another example. Look at the binomial $d^2 - 64$. d^2 is the square of d. And 64 is the square of 8. One square (64) is being subtracted from another square (d^2). The answer will be the difference between two squares. To find the factors of this type of binomial, follow the steps below.

Step 1. Take the square root of both terms. (Remember, the symbol $\sqrt{}$ stands for "the square root of.") Use your calculator to find the square root of 64, or look in the table on pages 257–260.

$$\sqrt{d^2} = d \qquad\qquad \sqrt{64} = 8$$

Step 2. Make two binomials from the square roots. One will be one square root plus the other square root. The other will be one square root minus the other square root.

$$(d^2 - 64) = (d + 8)(d - 8)$$

The factors of $d^2 - 64$ are $(d + 8) \bullet (d - 8)$.

Let's try factoring another example.

Example 3

$$16n^2 - 25$$

Step 1. Take the square root of each term. In this example, you also need to find the square root of the coefficient.

$$\sqrt{16n^2} = 4n \qquad\qquad \sqrt{25} = 5$$

Step 2. Make two binomials from the square roots. One binomial should use addition. The other binomial should use subtraction.

$$16n^2 - 25 = (4n + 5)(4n - 5)$$

The factors of $16n^2 - 25$ are $(4n + 5)$ and $(4n - 5)$.

■ PRACTICE 53: The Difference Between Two Squares

Factor each binomial below. Write your answer on the line after each binomial.

Example: $25x^2 - 16 =$

$\sqrt{25x^2} = 5x$ $\qquad$ $\sqrt{16} = 4$

$(5x + 4)(5x - 4)$

1. $y^2 - 81 =$ _____

2. $1 - b^2 =$ _____

3. $144r^2 - 49 =$ _____

4. $s^2 - 225 =$ _____

5. $64 - 9k^2 =$ _____

6. $100x^2 - 289 =$ _____

7. $16x^2 - 64 =$ _____

Factoring Trinomials

A binomial is a polynomial with two terms. A trinomial is a polynomial with three terms.

When you learned to multiply binomials, you used the FOIL method. Use the FOIL method to multiply $(x+y)(x+y)$.

First terms—$(x+y)(x+y) = x^2 \ldots$

Outside terms—$(x+y)(x+y) = x^2 + xy \ldots$

Inside terms—$(x+y)(x+y) = x^2 + xy + xy \ldots$

Last terms—$(x+y)(x+y) = x^2 + xy + xy + y^2$

Collect like terms to complete the problem.

$$x^2 + 2xy + y^2$$

Notice that when you multiply two binomials, your answer is a trinomial (a polynomial with three terms). When you try to factor a trinomial, you may find that many trinomials do not share a common factor. To factor trinomials like these, you must reverse the FOIL method. This will help you find the two binomials that were multiplied together to make the trinomial.

Example 1

Look at the following problem.

$$z^2 + 9z + 14 = (?+?)(?+?)$$

Step 1. When you use the FOIL method, multiplying the first term in each binomial gives you the first term in the trinomial answer.

Therefore, to find the factors of a trinomial, you must first find out what two terms can be multiplied together to give you the first term in the trinomial.

In this example, z^2 is the first term in the trinomial. What two terms can you multiply together to get z^2? z times z equals z^2. Make z the first term in both of your binomial factors.

$$z^2 + 9z + 14 = (z + ?)(z + ?)$$

Step 2. Now you want to find the last term for both binomial factors. When you multiply these two numbers together, you will get the last number in the trinomial (14). However, these two factors must also add together to form the coefficient of the trinomial's middle term (9). So you must find two factors of 14 that also add together to form 9. What are some factors of 14? 1 and 14 are factors of 14, but 1 plus 14 doesn't equal 9. How about 2 and 7? $2 \cdot 7 = 14$. And $2 + 7 = 9$! Make 2 and 7 the last terms in your binomial factors.

$$z^2 + 9z + 14 = (z + 2)(z + 7)$$

Now look at another example.

Example 2

$$m^2 + 10m + 16 = (? + ?)(? + ?)$$

Step 1. The first term is easy: $m \cdot m = m^2$. Make m the first term in each binomial.

$$m^2 + 10m + 16 = (m + ?)(m + ?)$$

Step 2. Now, what two factors of 16 add up to 10? 1 and 16? 4 and 4? How about 2 and 8? $2 \cdot 8 = 16$. And 2 plus 8 equals 10. Make 2 and 8 the second terms in the binomial factors of $m^2 + 10m + 16$.

$$m^2 + 10m + 16 = (m + 2)(m + 8)$$

The factors of $m^2 + 10m + 16$ are $(m + 2) \cdot (m + 8)$.

Here is the first rule for factoring trinomials.

> ### First Rule for Factoring Trinomials
>
> If the middle and last terms of a trinomial are positive, then the last terms in each binomial will also be positive.

THINK ABOUT IT

Look at the example from above: $m^2 + 10m + 16 = (m + 2)(m + 8)$. Do you have to put the 2 in the first binomial and the 8 in the second binomial? Or could you put the 2 in the second binomial and the 8 in the first binomial? Write your answer on a separate sheet of paper.

■ PRACTICE 54: Factoring Trinomials

Factor each trinomial into binomial factors. Write each answer on the line.

Example: $y^2 + 8y + 15 = (y + 5)(y + 3)$

$5(3) = 15$

$5 + 3 = 8$

$(y + 5)(y + 3)$

1. $u^2 + 7u + 12 = $ _____

2. $m^2 + 8m + 12 = $ _____

3. $k^2 + 13k + 40 = $ _____

4. $m^2 + 16m + 28 = $ _____

5. $s^2 + 5s + 6 = $ _____

6. $x^2 + 7x + 10 = $ _____

Factoring Trinomials with Negative Terms

You can use the same steps to factor a trinomial with a negative term that you used when you factored a trinomial with all positive terms.

Example 1

Look at the following trinomial.

$$r^2 - 5r + 6$$

Step 1. The factors of r^2 are r and r. Fill the first terms in the two factors with r. Don't put in any signs yet.

$$r^2 - 5r + 6 = (r \quad)(r \quad)$$

Step 2. The last two terms of the factors should multiply to equal +6. They should also add up to –5. Notice that the middle term is a negative number and the last term is a positive number. A negative number times a positive number equals a negative number. A negative number times another negative number equals a positive number. Because the last term of the trinomial is a positive number, the last terms of its binomial factors must both be negative. Fill in the signs.

$$r^2 - 5r + 6 = (r - ?)(r - ?)$$

Step 3. Now you need to find two negative factors of 6 that add up to −5. Does the sum of −1 and −6 equal −5? No. How about −2 plus −3? −2 • −3 = 6. And −2 + −3 = −5. Fill in the numbers.

$$r^2 - 5r + 6 = (r - 2)(r - 3)$$

Look at one more example.

Example 3

$$c^2 - 9c + 18$$

Step 1. The factors of c^2 are c and c. Make c the first term of each binomial factor.

$$c^2 - 9c + 18 = (c \quad)(c \quad)$$

Step 2. The middle term of the trinomial is negative. The last term is positive. That means that the last terms in both binomial factors must be negative.

$$c^2 - 9c + 18 = (c - ?)(c - ?)$$

Step 3. Now, what two negative factors of 18 add up to −9? −2 and −9? No. −6 and −3? Yes. −6 (−3) = 18. And −6 + −3 = −9. Make −6 and −3 the last terms of each binomial.

$$c^2 - 9c + 18 = (c - 6)(c - 3)$$

Here is a second rule for factoring trinomials.

Second Rule for Factoring Trinomials

If the middle term of a trinomial equation is negative and the last term is positive, the last term in both binomial factors will be negative.

 **TIP**

Any time you factor, you can check your work. Just multiply the factors together to see if the answer is the original polynomial.

■ PRACTICE 55: Factoring Trinomials with Negative Terms

Factor each trinomial into binomial factors. Write each answer on the line.

Example: $y^2 - 12y + 36 = (y - 6)(y - 6)$

$(y - ?)(y - ?)$

$-6(-6) = +36, -6 + -6 = -12$

$(y - 6)(y - 6)$

1. $u^2 - 7u + 10 = $ _____

2. $y^2 - 19y + 84 = $ _____

3. $k^2 - 25k + 156 = $ _____

4. $m^2 - 19m + 60 = $ _____

5. $z^2 - 9z + 20 = $ _____

Factoring Other Negative Trinomials

So far you have learned two important facts about trinomial factoring. You learned that when the middle and last terms of the trinomial are positive, both binomial factors involve addition.

$$x^2 + 6x + 8 = (x + 4)(x + 2)$$

You also learned that when the middle term is negative and the last term is positive, both binomial factors involve subtraction.

$$x^2 - 6x + 8 = (x - 4)(x - 2)$$

Now, what if the last term is negative?

Look at the following example.

Example 1

$$t^2 + 3t - 4$$

Step 1. The middle term in the trinomial above is positive. The last term is negative. What do these two facts tell you about the last terms in the polynomial factors?

The last term in the trinomial is negative. You know that this last term is the product of the last two terms in its binomial factors. Because it is negative, you know that one of those terms must be negative and the other must be positive. A negative number times a positive number equals a negative number. Now you can fill in the first term. You can also fill in the signs of the binomial factors.

$$t^2 + 3t - 4 = (t +)(t -)$$

Step 2. Now you must find the factors of –4. You know that one number must be positive and the other must be negative. The numbers must also add up to equal +3.

It's time to review the rules for adding positive and negative numbers! When you add a positive number and a negative number, you subtract the absolute values of the two numbers. Then you keep the sign of the number with the larger absolute value.

The middle term of the polynomial in this example is positive. That means that the factor with the larger absolute value must be positive.

What two factors of –4 add up to +3? How about +4 and –1? $+4(-1) = -4$. And +4 plus (–1) equals 3. You have already put the positive and negative signs into the binomials. Now fill in the numbers.

$$t^2 + 3t - 4 = (t + 4)(t - 1)$$

Let's look at another example.

Example 2

$$m^2 - 2m - 15$$

Step 1. In this example, you know that the first term of each binomial factor is m. $m \cdot m = m^2$. Because the last term is negative, one binomial must be positive and the other binomial must be negative.

$$m^2 - 2m - 15 = (m + ?)(m - ?)$$

Step 2. The coefficient of the middle term in the trinomial is negative. This means that the factor of 15 with the largest absolute value must also be negative. 3 and –5 are factors of 15. Does 3 plus –5 equal –2? Yes. Make 3 and –5 the last terms in your binomials. You've already put the signs in, so put 5 with the minus sign and 3 with the plus sign.

$$m^2 - 2m - 15 = (m + 3)(m - 5)$$

Here is the third rule for factoring trinomials.

Third Rule for Factoring Trinomials

If the last term of a trinomial is negative, the last term in one of the binomial factors will be positive, and the last term in the other binomial factor will be negative.

TIP

The distributive property is very important in algebra. This **property** says that for any three whole numbers (x, y, and z), $x(y + z) = (x)(y) + (x)(z)$. You may not realize it, but you have already used the distributive property. Can you find an example of the distributive property in this lesson?

■ PRACTICE 56: Factoring Other Negative Trinomials

Factor each trinomial on the next page. Write your answer on the line after each trinomial.

Example: $v^2 - 18v - 88 = (v - 22)(v + 4)$

$(v - ?)(v + ?)$

$-22(4) = -88, (-22) + 4 = -18$

$(v - 22)(v + 4)$

1. $f^2 + 2f - 15 =$ _____

2. $q^2 - 4q - 96 =$ _____

3. $x^2 + 9x - 22 =$ _____

4. $n^2 - 12n - 220 =$ _____

5. $s^2 + 3s - 180 =$ _____

6. $b^2 - 6b - 55 =$ _____

Factoring More Difficult Trinomials

So far you have been factoring trinomials that have a coefficient of 1 for the first term. (Remember, if there is a 1 before a variable, you don't write the 1. $1x$ is the same as x.) Now you will learn to factor when the first term has some other coefficient.

Example 1

Look at the trinomial below.

$$2x^2 + 5x + 3$$

In this trinomial, you must think of the different factors of both 3 and $2x^2$ to see which combination will give you $5x$ in the middle term. You must work harder since there are many possible numbers to use.

Step 1. First, you must factor the first term ($2x^2$) into $(2x) \cdot (x)$.

$$2x^2 + 5x + 3 = (2x\ )(x\ )$$

Step 2. Because the second and third terms are positive, you know that the last terms in both binomials are also positive. Write positive signs in both binomials.

$$2x^2 + 5x + 3 = (2x + ?)(x + ?)$$

Step 3. Factor the last term. The positive factors of 3 are 3 and 1. These are the only possible positive factors for 3. So where do you put 3, and where do you put 1?

Step 4. Check each possible combination. Try putting 1 in the binomial with $2x$ and 3 in the binomial with x. Will this work? Use the FOIL method to check.

$$(2x + 1)(x + 3)$$

$$2x^2 + 6x + x + 3$$

$$2x^2 + 7x + 3$$

No, this is not the original trinomial. The middle term should be $5x$, not $7x$. Try putting 3 in the binomial with $2x$ and 1 in the binomial with x. Use the FOIL method to check if this is correct.

$$(2x + 3)(x + 1)$$

$$2x^2 + 2x + 3x + 3$$

$$2x^2 + 5x + 3$$

Yes, this is the original trinomial.

The correct factors of $2x^2 + 5x + 3$ are $(2x + 3) \bullet (x + 1)$.

In the example above, the only possible factors for the first term ($2x^2$) were $2x$ and x. This made the problem easy! Sometimes both the first and last terms of a trinomial can have many different factors.

Look at the example below.

Example 2

$$8w^2 - 8w + 2$$

Step 1. Factor the first term. If the first term is positive, both factors will be positive.

$$8w^2 = 8w \bullet w$$

$$8w^2 = 4w \bullet 2w$$

Step 2. Because the middle term is negative and the last term is positive, you know that the last terms of both binomial factors must be negative (rule 2).

$$(? - ?)(? - ?)$$

Step 3. Factor the last term (2). You already put negative signs in both factors (step 2). So you know that you will be using only negative factors.

$$2 = (-1) \bullet (-2)$$

$$2 = (-2) \bullet (-1)$$

Step 4. You have identified all the possible first and last terms. Now you must find out which combination gives you the correct middle term.

$$(8w - 1)(w - 2)$$

$$(8w - 2)(w - 1)$$

$$(4w - 1)(2w - 2)$$

$$(4w - 2)(2w - 1)$$

Step 5. Test each combination of factors. To do this, multiply each inside and outside term. Then add them together. See which one gives you an answer of $-8w$. This is the middle term in the trinomial.

$(8w-1)(w-2)$

$-16w-w=-17w$

NO

$(8w-2)(w-1)$

$-8w-2w=-10w$

NO

$(4w-1)(2w-2)$

$-8w-2w=-10w$

NO

$(4w-2)(2w-1)$

$4w-4w=-8w$

YES

Now you know that the factors for $8w^2-8w+2$ are $(4w-2) \bullet (2w-1)$.

Try another example.

Example 3

$$4m^2 + 16m + 15$$

Step 1. Factor the first term $(4m^2)$. Since the coefficient of the first term is positive, you know that both factors must also be positive.

$$4m^2 = 4m \bullet m$$

$$4m^2 = 2m \bullet 2m$$

Step 2. Because both the middle and last terms are positive, you know that the binomial factors will both be positive.

$$(? + ?)\,(? + ?)$$

Step 3. Factor the last term (15). You already put positive signs in both factors (step 2), so you will be using only positive numbers.

$$15 = 15 \bullet 1$$
$$15 = 5 \bullet 3$$

Step 4. Make a list of all possible first terms and last terms.

$$(4m + 1)\,(m + 15)$$
$$(4m + 15)\,(m + 1)$$
$$(4m + 3)\,(m + 5)$$
$$(4m + 5)\,(m + 3)$$
$$(2m + 1)\,(2m + 15)$$
$$(2m + 3)\,(2m + 5)$$

Step 5. Test each set of inside and outside terms. Multiply the outside and inside terms of all six possible pairs. Then add their products together. Only one combination will give you the correct middle term ($+16m$).

$$(4m + 1)\,(m + 15) \longrightarrow 60m + m = 61m$$
$$(4m + 15)\,(m + 1) \longrightarrow 4m + 15m = 19m$$
$$(4m + 3)\,(m + 5) \longrightarrow 20m + 3m = 23m$$
$$(4m + 5)\,(m + 3) \longrightarrow 12m + 5m = 17m$$
$$(2m + 1)\,(2m + 15) \longrightarrow 30m + 2m = 32m$$
$$(2m + 3)\,(2m + 5) \longrightarrow 10m + 6m = 16m$$

The factors for $4m^2 + 16m + 15$ are $(2m+3) \cdot (2m+5)$.

There is no trick for solving difficult trinomials. You just need to practice!

■ PRACTICE 57: Factoring More Difficult Trinomials

Factor each trinomial. Write your answer on the line after each trinomial.

1. $7v^2 + 9v + 2 =$ _____

2. $2s^2 + 9s + 4 =$ _____

3. $10z^2 - 3z - 1 =$ _____

4. $6t^2 - 7t - 5 =$ _____

Combining Factoring Skills

You have now learned three methods of factoring:

1. finding the greatest common factor
2. factoring the difference of two squares
3. factoring trinomials

Complete factoring is when you apply all possible ways to factor an expression so that it cannot be factored any further. You may have to use several methods of factoring to completely factor an expression.

Example 1

Look at the trinomial below.

$$4m^3 + 24m^2 + 32m$$

Step 1. Does this trinomial have a greatest common factor? All the terms in the trinomial can be divided by $4m$. Factor out $4m$.

$$(4m)(m^2 + 6m + 8)$$

Now the original trinomial has been factored into a monomial $(4m)$ and a less complex trinomial $(m^2 + 6m + 8)$.

Step 2. The trinomial $m^2 + 6m + 8$ can be factored into two binomials.

$$(m^2 + 6m + 8) = (m + ?)(m + ?)$$

Find the last term for each binomial. The factors of 8 are $8 \bullet 1$ and $2 \bullet 4$. Which set of factors will give you the correct middle term?

$$8 \bullet 1 = 8; \; 8 + 1 = 9$$
$$4 \bullet 2 = 8; \; 4 + 2 = 6$$

The factors 4 and 2 equal 8 when multiplied. They also equal 6 when added. 4 and 2 must be the last terms of the factors.

$$(m^2 + 6m + 8) = (m + 4)(m + 2)$$

Step 3. Now combine the binomial factors with the greatest common factor of the original trinomial.

$$(4m)(m + 4)(m + 2)$$

The trinomial is now completely factored.

Look at another example.

Example 2

$$27b^3 - 27b$$

Step 1. Does this binomial have a greatest common factor? Both $27b^3$ and $-27b$ can be divided by $27b$. Factor out $27b$.

$$(27b)(b^2 - 1)$$

Step 2. Notice that the binomial $b^2 - 1$ is the difference between two squares. Remember, the first factor of the difference between two squares always equals the square root of the first term plus the square root of the second term. And the second factor always equals the square root of the first term minus the square root of the second term.

$$(b + 1)(b - 1)$$

Step 3. Now combine the binomial factors with the greatest common factor of the original trinomial.

$$(27b)(b + 1)(b - 1)$$

The trinomial is now completely factored.

THINK ABOUT IT

Erica thinks she has reached the final step in factoring the binomial $(16h)(h^2 - 1)$. Is the binomial completely factored? If not, what needs to be done? Write your answer on a separate sheet of paper.

■ PRACTICE 58: Combining Factoring Skills

Factor the following expressions. Make sure each expression is factored completely. Write your answer on the line.

1. $2n^2 - 2 =$ _____

2. $3r^2 + 9r + 6 =$ _____

3. $3t^2 - 36t + 105 = $ _____

4. $2s^3 - 72s = $ _____

5. $2y^3 - 26y^2 + 72y = $ _____

6. $100n^2 - 400 = $ _____

UNIT 4 REVIEW
Circle the correct answer for each question or problem below.

1. Add these monomials: $8xy + 16xy$.
   a. $8xy$ **b.** $8x^2y^2$
   c. $24xy$ **d.** $16x^2y^2$

2. Which polynomial below is in the correct order?
   a. $1 - 6w + 5w^2$ **b.** $12p - 10p^2 + 5p^3$
   c. $20m + 10m^2$ **d.** $5b^2 - 10b + 20$

3. Add these polynomials together: $3x^3 + 4x^2$ and $-7x - 12x^3 - 7x^2$. Make sure your answer is in the correct order.
   a. $3x^2 + 9x^3 - 7x$ **b.** $9x^2 - 3x^3 - 7x$
   c. $-3x^3 - 9x^2 + 7x$ **d.** $-9x^3 - 3x^2 - 7x$

4. Multiply the following monomials: $(-6x^2)(-7x^4)$.
   a. $-42x^8$ **b.** $42x^8$
   c. $-42x^6$ **d.** $42x^6$

5. $5n^3$ is a simplification of which of the following?
   a. $\dfrac{3n^6}{15n^9}$ **b.** $\dfrac{12n^6}{5n^{12}}$
   c. $\dfrac{-15n^{12}}{3n^9}$ **d.** $\dfrac{30n^{12}}{6n^9}$

6. Multiply these binomials using the FOIL method: $(4x + 2)$ $(5x + 7)$.

    a. $14x^2 + 10x + 28$ **b.** $28x^2 + 34x + 14$

    c. $10x^2 + 14x + 28$ **d.** $20x^2 + 38x + 14$

7. Look at the trinomial: $72y^3 + 48y^2 - 96y$. What is the greatest common factor of this trinomial?

    a. $24y$ **b.** $24y^2$

    c. $48y$ **d.** $48y^2$

8. Look at the trinomial: $d^2 - 45d + 450$. What are the factors for this trinomial?

    a. $(d - 30)(d - 15)$ **b.** $(45d - 10)(10d - 3)$

    c. $(d + 30)(d - 15)$ **d.** $(45d + 1)(10d - 1)$

9. Look at the trinomial: $5b^2 - 11b - 12$. What are the factors for this trinomial?

    a. $(5b + 1)(b - 12)$ **b.** $(5b + 4)(b - 3)$

    c. $(5b + 6)(b - 2)$ **d.** $(5b + 3)(b - 4)$

10. Look at this binomial: $16x^3 - 36x$. Which set of terms below are the factors of this binomial?

    a. $(9x)(2x + 3)(3x - 2)$ **b.** $(4x)(2x + 3)(2x - 3)$

    c. $(3x)(4x + 4)(4x - 9)$ **d.** $(2x)(4x + 4)(4x - 9)$

UNIT 4 APPLICATION ACTIVITY 1

Planning a Party

Algebra can help you plan a party! Suppose you are planning a big party. You have $30 to spend on snacks and drinks. First, make a list of two kinds of drinks and two kinds of snacks you want to buy. Make your list below.

Drinks   **Snacks**

1. _____   1. _____

2. _____   2. _____

Next, visit a food store or find a flyer from the store. Find out how much one package of each drink and snack costs. Write the costs below:

Cost for drink 1: _____   **Cost for snack 1:** _____

Cost for drink 2: _____   **Cost for snack 2:** _____

Now, make a spending plan for your $30. Use an algebraic equation to figure out how many packages of each drink and snack you can buy. The variable (x) will stand for the number of packages you can buy. For example, suppose you want to figure out how many bottles of soda you can buy with $5. If the soda costs $1.20 per container, you would write $1.20x = 5$. In this equation, $x = 4r80$. Ignore the remainder (you cannot buy part of a bottle of soda). You can buy 4 bottles of soda.

- Suppose you want to spend $10 on drinks. You decide to spend half of that, or $5, on each type of drink.

Equation for drink 1: _____   **Equation for drink 2:** _____

Solve for x: _____   **Solve for x:** _____

How many can you buy? _____ **How many can you buy?** _____

- You have $20 left. You decide to spend $10 on each type of snack.

Equation for snack 1: _____   Equation for snack 2: _____

Solve for x: _____   Solve for x: _____

How many can you buy? _____   How many can you buy? _____

UNIT 4 APPLICATION ACTIVITY 2

Car Washes and Bake Sales

Most clubs, organizations, and schools plan at least one fund-raising event each year to raise money. This money helps pay for the group's activities. Talk to members of four civic clubs, organizations, or classes in your town. Find out what kind of fund-raisers they are planning. What will they sell, or what service will they provide? How much will they charge?

When you have this information, think of equations you can use to find the total amount of money each group will make from their fund-raisers. For example, suppose one group is planning a car wash and a cookie sale. For the car wash, they plan to charge $4 per car. For the cookie sale, they plan to charge $3 per box. How much money will this group make? There are two things you do not know: the number of cars the group will wash, and the number of boxes (of cookies) the group will sell. These will be your two variables: x (number of cars washed) and y (number of boxes sold). The amount of money they will make at the car wash is $4 times the number of cars, or $4x$. The amount of money they will make at the cookie sale is $3 times the number of boxes, or $3y$. Put these variables into an equation: $4x + 3y = ?$

Now think of equations for your groups. Write the information below.

	Name	Fund-Raisers	Equation
Group 1:	_____	_____	_____
		_____	
Group 2:	_____	_____	_____
		_____	
Group 3:	_____	_____	_____
		_____	
Group 4:	_____	_____	_____
		_____	

UNIT 5

Quadratic Equations

LESSON 13: Quadratic Equations

GOAL: To learn to use factoring to solve quadratic equations

WORDS TO KNOW

perfect square quadratic equation

quadratic equation

What Is a Quadratic Equation?

The word *quadratic* means "squared." A **quadratic equation** is an equation in which at least one term is squared—that is, it has a power of 2. No term in a quadratic equation has a power greater than 2. And a quadratic equation has only one variable. Just remember the following:

Quadratic Equations

1. have at least one term that has an exponent of 2
2. never have exponents higher than 2
3. have only one variable or unknown

Here are some examples of quadratic equations.

$$4x^2 + 8x + 12 = 0$$

$$x^2 - 10x + 24 = 0$$

$$x^2 - 9 = 0$$

Now look at the equations below and on the next page. These are not quadratic equations.

- $x^2 + 2xy - 7 = 0$ This is not a quadratic equation because it has more than one variable.

- $12w - 5 = 0$ This is not a quadratic equation because it has no terms with an exponent of 2.

- $x^4 - 10x^3 + 11x - 24 = 0$ This is not a quadratic equation because it has terms with exponents that are higher than 2.

Quadratic equations follow this general form:

$$ax^2 + bx + c = 0$$

The letters a and b in the formula stand for the coefficients in the equation. The letter c stands for the constant term.

Example 1

Look at the equation below.

$$4x^2 + 8x + 12 = 0$$

In this equation, $a = 4$, $b = 8$, $c = 12$.

Example 2

Now look at this equation.

$$x^2 - 10x + 24 = 0$$

In the equation above, $a = 1$, $b = -10$, and $c = 24$.

Example 3

Let's look at one more.

$$x^2 - 9 = 0$$

In this equation, we can see that $a = 1$ and $c = 9$. But how do we decide on the value for b? We can use 0 as the value of b without changing the equation.

$$x^2 + 0x - 9 = 0$$

In this equation, $a = 1$, $b = 0$, and $c = -9$.

■ PRACTICE 59: What Is a Quadratic Equation?

Look at the equations below. Decide whether or not each one is a quadratic equation. If it is, write "yes" on the line after the equation. If it is not a quadratic equation, write "no." Then, for those equations that are quadratic, write the a, b, and c coefficients.

Example: $x^2 + 14x - 12 = 0$ yes

$a = 1$ $b = 14$ $c = -12$

1. $x^2 + y^2 = 0$ _____ _____

2. $x - 13 = 0$ _____ _____

3. $13x^3 - 27 = 0$ _____ _____

4. $x^2 - 125 = 0$ _____ _____

5. $3x^2 + 2y - 9 = 0$ _____ _____

6. $4x^3 - 64x^2 - 144y = 0$ _____ _____

7. $64x^2 - 144 = 0$ _____ _____

8. $x^2 + 4x + 4 = 0$ _____ _____

Zero Products

You already know that if you multiply any number by 0, the product is 0. Look at the examples below.

$$26 \bullet 0 = 0$$

$$\frac{3}{5} \bullet 0 = 0$$

$$0 \bullet -327 = 0$$

Sometimes an algebraic equation will equal 0. If the constant—the known number—is not 0, then the unknown number must be 0.

Example 1

Look at the following equation.

$$k \bullet 9 = 0$$

In this equation, you know that 9 does not equal 0. The only number that you can multiply by 9 to equal 0 is 0. The variable k must equal 0.

Example 2

Look at the equation below.

$$-56 \bullet w = 0$$

Again, since the answer is 0, you know that w must equal 0.

Sometimes an equation with two variables will equal 0. When this happens, you know that either one or both variables is equal to 0.

Look at the example below.

Example 3

$$p \bullet q = 0$$

In this equation, either p or q, or both p and q, must equal 0.

■ PRACTICE 60: Zero Products

Solve each equation below. Write each answer on the line.

1. $x \bullet 76 = 0$

$x =$ _____

2. $t \bullet -5 = 0$

$t =$ _____

3. $m^2 \bullet 21 = 0$

$m =$ _____

4. $p \bullet \dfrac{3}{8} = 0$

$p =$ _____

Making Quadratic Equations Equal Zero

On page 216, you learned that quadratic equations can be written in the form $ax^2 + bx + c = 0$. In this form, quadratic equations are easy to solve. But what do you do if a quadratic equation is written in a different form? When that happens, your first step is to move the equation around so that it equals 0.

Example 1

For instance, look at the quadratic equation $16x^2 + 24x = -9$. There is a negative number (–9) on the right side of this equation. The first step in solving the equation is to get rid of the –9. To do this, add 9 to both sides of the equation.

$$16x^2 + 24x = -9$$

$$16x^2 + 24x + 9 = -9 + 9$$

$$16x^2 + 24x + 9 = 0$$

Sometimes there will be a term with a variable on the right side of the equation. When this happens, you must get rid of it by either adding or subtracting.

Look at the example below.

Example 2

$$16x^2 + 9 = -24x$$

In this equation, $-24x$ is on the right side of the equation. You want to get rid of $-24x$. To do this, add $24x$ to both sides of the equation.

$$16x^2 + 24x + 9 = -24x + 24x$$

$$16x^2 + 24x + 9 = 0$$

TIP

Remember to put polynomials in the correct order. The term with the highest exponent should be first. The term with the second highest exponent should be second, and so on. Terms that are just numbers (with no variables) should be last.

■ PRACTICE 61: Making Quadratic Equations Equal Zero

Make each of the following equations equal zero. Write each new equation on the line.

Example: $2x^2 - 18 = 14x$

$$2x^2 - 18 - 14x = 14x - 14x$$

$$2x^2 - 14x - 18 = 0$$

1. $16x^2 = 49$

_____

2. $12x^2 + 25x = -12$

_____

3. $2x + 7 = -x^2$

_____

4. $9x^2 + 9 = -18x$

_____

5. $4x^2 = 81$

_____

6. $3x^2 + 4x = 50$

_____

Solving Special Binomial Quadratic Equations

After you move all the terms in a quadratic equation to the left side and make the right side equal to 0, you can solve some quadratic equations by factoring. Factoring means breaking a polynomial into parts. The parts will include binomials, terms, and constants.

If you factor the left side of a quadratic equation into two parts, you can multiply these two parts and still get zero on the right side. This means that one or both of the factors must equal zero.

Example 1

Look at the equation below.

$$x^2 - 16 = 0$$

This is a quadratic equation. It has only one variable. It has one term with an exponent of 2. None of its terms has an exponent that is greater than 2.

You want to solve this equation by factoring. To do this, follow these steps.

Step 1. The left side of the quadratic equation is a binomial. It is also the difference between two squares. This sort of binomial can always be factored into two binomials. The first binomial is the square root of the first term minus the square root of the second term. The second binomial is the square root of the first term plus the square root of the second term.

$$(x-4)(x+4) = 0$$

Step 2. Because the product of the two binomials is 0, you know that either $(x-4) = 0$ or $(x+4) = 0$. This means that

$x - 4 = 0$		$x + 4 = 0$
$x - 4 + 4 = 0 + 4$	or	$x + 4 - 4 = 0 - 4$
$x = 4$		$x = -4$

If $x = -4$, the factor $(x+4)$ equals 0. $-4 + 4 = 0$. If $x = 4$, the factor $(x-4)$ also equals 0. $4 - 4 = 0$. So this equation has more than one solution. The solutions to the equation $x^2 + 16 = 0$ are -4 and 4.

Let's look at another example.

Example 2

$$4x^2 = 49$$

Step 1. Move all the terms to the left side of the equation. Subtract 49 from both sides of the equation.

$$4x^2 - 49 = 49 - 49$$

$$4x^2 - 49 = 0$$

Step 2. This quadratic equation is the difference between two squares. It can be factored into two binomials. The first binomial is the square root of the first term minus the square root of the second term. The second binomial is the square root of the first term plus the square root of the second term.

$$(2x - 7)(2x + 7) = 0$$

Step 3. Because the product of the two binomials is 0, you know that either $(2x - 7) = 0$ or $(2x + 7) = 0$. Get rid of the 7 in each factor.

$$2x - 7 = 0 \qquad\qquad 2x + 7 = 0$$

$$2x - 7 + 7 = 0 + 7 \quad \text{or} \quad 2x + 7 - 7 = 0 - 7$$

$$2x = 7 \qquad\qquad 2x = -7$$

Step 4. Now divide both sides of each equation by 2 to solve for x.

$$2x = 7 \qquad\qquad\qquad 2x = -7$$

$$\frac{2x}{2} = \frac{7}{2} = 3\frac{1}{2} \quad \text{or} \quad \frac{2x}{2} = \frac{7}{2} = -3\frac{1}{2}$$

The solutions to the quadratic equation $4x^2 = 49$ are $3\dfrac{1}{2}$ and $-3\dfrac{1}{2}$.

■ TIP

It might be a good idea to review some basic algebra terms. Do you remember what the difference between two squares is? Look at the phrase carefully. It means that one "square" is being subtracted from another "square." Look at this example: $x^2 - 16 = 0$. x^2 is a "square" ($x \bullet x = x^2$). 16 is also a "square" ($4 \bullet 4 = 16$). So, $x^2 - 16 = 0$ is the difference between two squares.

Now, what is a binomial? Remember that a monomial is an expression with only one term. For example: $2mp^2$. A binomial has two terms: $2mp^2 + 3p$. A trinomial has three terms: $2mp^2 + 3p + 6$.

Be sure to review all your basic algebra terms. It will make learning much easier!

■ PRACTICE 62: Solving Special Binomial Quadratic Equations

Solve the quadratic equations on the next page. You may need to use another sheet of paper to do the work. Then write each answer on the line.

Example: $9x^2 + 225 = 450$

$9x^2 + 225 - 450 = 450 - 450$

$9x^2 - 225 = 0$

$(3x + 15)(3x - 15) = 0$

$$3x + 15 = 0 \qquad\qquad 3x - 15 = 0$$

$$3x + 15 - 15 = 0 - 15 \quad \text{or} \quad 3x - 15 + 15 = 0 + 15$$

$$3x = -15 \qquad\qquad 3x = 15$$

$$x = -5 \qquad\qquad x = +5$$

1. $x^2 - 100 = 0$

$x =$ _____

2. $x^2 - 25 = 0$

$x =$ _____

3. $25x^2 - 32 = 32$

$x =$ _____

4. $9x^2 + 24 = 25$

$x =$ _____

Solving Perfect Square Quadratic Equations

Some quadratic equations are easy to solve. They can be factored into the square of a single binomial. These are called **perfect square quadratic equations.** These quadratic equations have only one solution.

Example 1

The following equation is an example of a perfect square quadratic equation:

$$4x^2 + 8x + 4 = 0$$

Step 1. When you factor this quadratic equation, you find that it is the square of one polynomial.

$$(2x + 2)(2x + 2) = 0$$

or

$$(2x + 2)^2 = 0$$

Step 2. The factors of this quadratic equation are exactly the same. Since you know that at least one of them must equal 0, you know that they both equal 0. So, you can assume that $2x + 2 = 0$. Get rid of the 2 by subtracting 2 from both sides of the equation.

$$2x + 2 - 2 = 0 - 2$$

$$2x = -2$$

Step 3. Divide both sides of the equation by 2 to solve for x.

$$\frac{2x}{2} = \frac{-2}{2}$$

$$x = -1$$

The solution to the equation $4x^2 + 8x + 4 = 0$ is $x = -1$.

Look at another example.

Example 2

$$16x^2 + 36 = 48x$$

Step 1. Get all the variables on the left. Subtract $48x$ from both sides of the equation.

$$16x^2 - 48x + 36 = 48x - 48x$$

$$16x^2 - 48x + 36 = 0$$

Step 2. Factor the equation. You will find that it is the square of one polynomial.

$$(4x - 6)(4x - 6) = 0$$

or

$$(4x - 6)^2 = 0$$

Step 3. Because both factors of the polynomial are the same, you can assume that $4x - 6 = 0$. To solve for x, get rid of the -6 on the left side of the equation. Add 6 to both sides.

$$4x - 6 + 6 = 0 + 6$$

$$4x = 6$$

Step 4. Divide both sides of the equation by 4.

$$\frac{4x}{4} = \frac{6}{4}$$

$$x = 1\frac{1}{2}$$

The solution to the equation $16x^2 - 48x + 36 = 0$ is $x = 1\frac{1}{2}$.

THINK ABOUT IT

Is the problem $3y^3 + 18y + 9 = 0$ a perfect square quadratic equation? Explain your answer below.

■ PRACTICE 63: Solving Perfect Square Quadratic Equations

Solve each perfect square equation below. You may need to use another sheet of paper to do your work. Write each answer on the line.

Example: $x^2 + 6x + 9 = 0$

$$(x + 3)(x + 3) = 0$$

$$x + 3 - 3 = 0 - 3$$

$$x = -3$$

1. $25x^2 - 40x = -16$

$x =$ _____

2. $9x^2 + 48x + 32 = -32$

$x =$ _____

3. $x^2 - 8x + 16 = 0$

$x =$ _____

4. $x^2 - 12x + 36 = 0$

$x =$ _____

5. $4x^2 + 24x + 24 = -12$

$x =$ _____

6. $x^2 - 10x + 25 = 0$

$x =$ _____

7. $x^2 - 6x + 9 = 0$

$x =$ _____

8. $64x^2 - 192x = -144$

$x =$ _____

Types of Quadratic Equations Solved by Factoring

Some quadratic equations cannot be solved by factoring. But many can be solved this way. Equations that can be solved by factoring follow certain patterns. So do their factors. You have already looked at some of these patterns. For example, if the second and third terms in the equation are both positive, then both binomial factors will have plus signs.

Example 1

$$x^2 + 35x + 276 = 0 \qquad \text{factors: } (x + 12)(x + 23)$$

Example 2

If the second term of the equation is positive and the third term is negative, then one factor will have a minus sign and one will have a plus sign.

$$y^2 + 3y - 700 = 0 \qquad \text{factors: } (y + 28)(y - 25)$$

Example 3

If the second and third terms of the equation are both negative, then one factor will have a minus sign and one will have a plus sign.

$$x^2 - 11x - 42 = 0 \qquad \text{factors: } (x - 14)(x + 3)$$

Example 4

If the second term of the equation is negative and the third term is positive, both binomial factors will have minus signs.

$$x^2 - 13x + 40 = 0 \qquad \text{factors: } (x - 5)(x - 8)$$

We can use these patterns to group quadratic equations solved by factoring into four types. Look at the chart on the next page to see these types.

Types of Quadratic Equations Solved by Factoring		
	If the structure of the equation is	**Then the binomial factors have the form**
Type A	$x^2 + bx + c = 0$ Second and third terms positive	$(x + ?)(x + ?) = 0$
Type B	$x^2 + bx - c = 0$ Second term positive, third term negative	$(x + ?)(x - ?) = 0$
Type C	$x^2 - bx - c = 0$ Second and third terms negative	$(x - ?)(x + ?) = 0$
Type D	$x^2 - bx + c = 0$ Second term negative, third term positive	$(x - ?)(x - ?) = 0$

■ PRACTICE 64: Types of Quadratic Equations Solved by Factoring

Look at the chart above. Use this chart to decide which type of quadratic equation is shown on the next page. Write the type (A, B, C, or D) on the line after each equation.

Example: $x^2 - x - 12 = 0$ C

1. $x^2 + 7x + 10 = 0$ _____

2. $x^2 + 5x - 24 = 0$ _____

3. $x^2 - 14x + 51 = 0$ _____

4. $x^2 + 7x + 12 = 0$ _____

5. $x^2 + 9x + 20 = 0$ _____

6. $x^2 + 4x - 21 = 0$ _____

7. $x^2 - 15x + 56 = 0$ _____

8. $x^2 - 14x + 24 = 0$ _____

9. $x^2 + 6x + 5 = 0$ _____

10. $x^2 - 15x + 54 = 0$ _____

11. $x^2 - 5x - 84 = 0$ _____

12. $x^2 + 21x + 54 = 0$ _____

Solving the Four Types of Quadratic Equations

Review the four types of quadratic equations, as shown in the chart on page 230. You can solve each type of quadratic equation the same way. First, you must find factors for the last term of the quadratic equation. These two factors added together must equal the coefficient of the second term in the equation.

Here is an example of a type A quadratic equation.

Example 1

$$x^2 + 8x + 15 = 0$$

Step 1. This is a type A quadratic equation because the second and third terms in the equation are positive. Its binomial factors have the following form:

$$(x + ?)(x + ?) = 0$$

Step 2. Look at the last term of the equation (15). Which two positive factors of 15 will add up to the middle coefficient (8)? The answer is 5 and 3.

$$5 \cdot 3 = 15$$
$$5 + 3 = 8$$

Step 3. Make 5 and 3 the second terms in the binomial factors of the quadratic equation.

$$(x + 5)(x + 3) = 0$$

Now you know that one of these two binomials must equal 0. Either $(x + 5) = 0$ or $(x + 3) = 0$.

Step 4. Find the value for x in both factors.

$x + 5 = 0$		$x + 3 = 0$
$x + 5 - 5 = 0 - 5$	or	$x + 3 - 3 = 0 - 3$
$x = -5$		$x = -3$

The solution to the equation $x^2 + 8x + 15 = 0$ is $x = -3$ or $x = -5$.

Here is an example of a type B quadratic equation.

Example 2

$$x^2 + 5x - 14 = 0$$

Step 1. This is a type B quadratic equation because the second term in the equation is positive and the third term is negative. Its binomial factors have the following form:

$$(x + ?)(x - ?) = 0$$

Step 2. Look at the last term (−14). Which two factors of −14 will add up to the middle coefficient (5)? The answer is 7 and −2.

$$7 \cdot (-2) = -14$$
$$7 + (-2) = 5$$

Step 3. Make −2 and 7 the second terms in the binomial factors of the quadratic equation.

$$(x + 7)(x - 2) = 0$$

Step 4. Find the value of x in both factors. Since the product is 0, you know that one of the binomials must equal 0. Either $(x + 7) = 0$ or $(x - 2) = 0$.

$x + 7 = 0$	or	$x - 2 = 0$
$x + 7 - 7 = 0 - 7$		$x - 2 + 2 = 0 + 2$
$x = -7$		$x = 2$

The solution to the equation $x^2 + 5x - 14 = 0$ is $x = 2$ or $x = -7$.

Here is an example of a type C quadratic equation.

Example 3

$$x^2 - 5x - 14 = 0$$

Step 1. This is a type C quadratic equation because both the second and third terms in the equation are negative. Its binomial factors have the following form:

$$(x - ?)(x + ?) = 0$$

Step 2. Look at the last term (–14). Which two factors of –14 will add up to the middle coefficient (–5)? The answer is –7 and 2.

$$-7 \cdot 2 = -14$$

$$-7 + 2 = -5$$

Step 3. Make –7 and 2 the second terms in the binomial factors of the quadratic equation.

$$(x - 7)(x + 2) = 0$$

Now you know that either $(x - 7) = 0$ or $(x + 2) = 0$.

Step 4. Find the value of x in both factors.

$$x - 7 = 0 \qquad\qquad x + 2 = 0$$

$$x - 7 + 7 = 0 + 7 \quad \text{or} \quad x + 2 - 2 = 0 - 2$$

$$x = 7 \qquad\qquad x = -2$$

The solution to the equation $x^2 + 5x - 14 = 0$ is $x = 7$ or $x = -2$.

Now let's look at an example of a type D quadratic equation.

Example 4

$$x^2 - 6x + 8 = 0$$

Step 1. This is a type D quadratic equation because the second term in the equation is negative and the third term is positive. Its binomial factors have the following form:

$$(x - ?)(x - ?) = 0$$

Step 2. Look at the last term (8). Which two factors of 8 will add up to the middle coefficient (–6)? The answer is –4 and –2.

$$-4 \cdot (-2) = 8$$
$$-4 + (-2) = -6$$

Step 3. Make –4 and –2 the second terms in the binomial factors of the quadratic equation.

$$(x - 4)(x - 2) = 0$$

Now you know that either $(x - 4) = 0$ or $(x - 2) = 0$.

Step 4. Find the value of x in both factors.

$$x - 4 = 0 \qquad\qquad x - 2 = 0$$
$$x - 4 + 4 = 0 + 4 \quad \text{or} \quad x - 2 + 2 = 0 + 2$$
$$x = 4 \qquad\qquad x = 2$$

The solution to the equation $x^2 - 6x + 8 = 0$ is $x = 4$ or $x = 2$.

Is $x^2 + 3x^3 - 10 = 0$ a type B equation? Why or why not? Write your answer on a separate sheet of paper.

■ PRACTICE 65: Solving the Four Types of Quadratic Equations

Decide which type of quadratic equation each of the following is. Then solve each equation by factoring. Write each answer on the line.

1. $x^2 + 9x + 8 = 0$ Type: _____

$x =$ _____ or _____

2. $x^2 + 5x - 6 = 0$ Type: _____

$x =$ _____ or _____

3. $x^2 - 5x + 6 = 0$ Type: _____

$x =$ _____ or _____

4. $x^2 - 2x - 8 = 0$ Type: _____

$x =$ _____ or _____

5. $x^2 + 13x + 30 = 0$ Type: _____

$x =$ _____ or _____

LESSON 14: The Quadratic Formula

GOAL: To learn to solve quadratic equations using factoring and the quadratic formula

WORDS TO KNOW

quadratic formula

The Quadratic Formula

Not all quadratic equations can be factored. This means that you can't solve all quadratic equations by factoring. Instead, you can use a special formula to solve these equations: the **quadratic formula.** The quadratic formula is used to solve quadratic equations that are very hard to factor.

Below is the general form of a quadratic equation.

$$ax^2 + bx + c = 0$$

Remember, a stands for the coefficient of the first term. b stands for the coefficient of the second term. And c stands for the constant. If either of the first two terms does not have a coefficient, use 1, because $1x = 1$.

To use the quadratic formula, you put the quadratic equation into the following form:

$$x = \frac{-b \pm \sqrt{b^2 - 4ac}}{2a}$$

The $\pm$ sign in the formula means that there are two possible solutions to each quadratic equation. Here is one solution.

$$x = \frac{-b + \sqrt{b^2 - 4ac}}{2a}$$

Here is the second solution.

$$x = \frac{-b - \sqrt{b^2 - 4ac}}{2a}$$

Example 1

Look at the equation $x^2 + 6x + 5 = 0$. You already know that this is a type A quadratic equation. One way to solve this equation is by factoring.

$$x^2 + 6x + 5 = 0$$

$$(x + ?)(x + ?)$$

$$5 \cdot 1 = 5$$

$$5 + 1 = 6$$

$$(x + 5)(x + 1) = 0$$

$$x = -5 \text{ or } -1$$

You can also solve it by using the quadratic formula. Look at the steps that follow.

Step 1. Find the a, b, and c coefficients in the quadratic equation.

$$x^2 + 6x + 5 = 0$$

$$a = 1 \qquad b = 6 \qquad c = 5$$

Step 2. Replace the letters in the formula with the correct numbers.

The value for *a* in this equation is 1. *a* is in the formula in two places. Replace *a* with 1.

$$x = \frac{-b \pm \sqrt{b^2 - 4(1)(c)}}{2(1)}$$

The value for *b* in this equation is 6. *b* is in the formula in two places. Replace *b* with 6.

$$x = \frac{-6 \pm \sqrt{6^2 - 4(1)(c)}}{2(1)}$$

The value for *c* in this equation is 5. *c* is in the formula in one place. Replace *c* with 5.

$$x = \frac{-6 \pm \sqrt{6^2 - 4(1)(5)}}{2(1)}$$

Step 3. Now do the math inside the square root sign. Then take the square root of the number you find. Use your calculator or the Table of Squares and Square Roots on pages 257–260.

$$x = \frac{-6 \pm \sqrt{36 - 20}}{2}$$

$$x = \frac{-6 \pm \sqrt{16}}{2}$$

$$x = \frac{-6 \pm 4}{2}$$

Step 4. Because of the plus or minus sign, you end up with two possible answers.

$$x = \frac{-6 - 4}{2} = -5$$

or

$$x = \frac{-6 + 4}{2} = -1$$

These are the same solutions for x you found by factoring.

Example 2

Now look at the quadratic equation below. This is a quadratic equation that cannot be factored.

$$2x^2 + 2 = -7x$$

Use the quadratic formula to find the solution to this equation. Before you start, make the equation equal to 0. Add $7x$ to both sides of the equation.

$$2x^2 + 7x + 2 = -7x + 7x$$

$$2x^2 + 7x + 2 = 0$$

Step 1. Find the a, b, and c coefficients in the quadratic equation.

$$2x^2 + 7x + 2 = 0$$

$$a = 2 \qquad b = 7 \qquad c = 2$$

Step 2. Replace the letters in the formula with the correct numbers.

$$x = \frac{-7 \pm \sqrt{7^2 - 4(2)(2)}}{2(2)}$$

Step 3. Do the math inside the square root sign. Then take the square root of the number you find.

$$x = \frac{-7 \pm \sqrt{49 - 16}}{4}$$

$$x = \frac{-7 \pm \sqrt{33}}{4}$$

Step 4. In this case, 33 is not a perfect square. It is not easy to simplify. Leave 33 under the square root sign. Because of the plus or minus sign, you end up with two answers.

$$x = \frac{-7 + \sqrt{33}}{4} \quad \text{and} \quad x = \frac{-7 - \sqrt{33}}{4}$$

Step 5. Check your answer. To do this, use your calculator or a square root table to find the square root of 33. Look at the Table of Squares and Square Roots on pages 257–260. The table shows you that $\sqrt{33} = 5.74$. What does x equal? Round off to the nearest .01.

$$x = \frac{-7 + 5.74}{4} = \qquad\qquad x = \frac{-7 - 5.74}{4} =$$

$$\frac{-1.26}{4} = -.315 \qquad\qquad \frac{-12.74}{4} = -3.185$$

round −.315 to −.32 $\qquad$ round −3.185 to −3.19

Substitute these two numbers (−.32 and −3.19) into the original equation. Then work out the arithmetic. Round off to the nearest tenth (.1).

$$2x^2 + 2 = -7x \qquad\qquad 2x^2 + 2 = -7x$$
$$2(-.32)^2 + 2 = -7(-.32) \qquad 2(-3.19)^2 + 2 = -7(-3.19)$$
$$2(.1024) + 2 = 2.24 \qquad\quad 2(10.18) + 2 = 22.33$$
$$2.2 = 2.2 \qquad\qquad\qquad 22.3 = 22.3$$

In both cases, the two sides remain equal to each other. This tells you that your answers are correct.

TIP

If you have a calculator with a square root key, you don't need a square root table. Just enter the number whose square root you want to find. Then hit the square root key. This will give you the answer.

■ PRACTICE 66: The Quadratic Formula

Use the quadratic formula to solve each quadratic equation on the next page. You may need to do the work on another sheet of paper. Then write each answer on the line.

Example: $2x^2 + 7x + 3 = 0$

$$a = 2,\ b = 7,\ c = 3$$

$$x = \frac{-7 \pm \sqrt{7^2 - 4(2)(3)}}{2(2)}$$

$$x = \frac{-7 \pm \sqrt{49 - 24}}{4}$$

$$x = \frac{-7 \pm \sqrt{25}}{4}$$

$$x = \frac{-7 + 5}{4} = -\frac{2}{4} = -\frac{1}{2}$$

or $\qquad x = \dfrac{-7 - 5}{4} = -\dfrac{12}{4} = -3$

$$x = -\dfrac{1}{2} \text{ or } -3$$

1. $2x^2 + 11x + 5 = 0$

$x =$ _____ or _____

2. $2x^2 + 15x + 7 = 0$

$x =$ _____ or _____

3. $3x^2 + 20x = -17$

$x =$ _____ or _____

4. $3x^2 + 12x = -9$

$x =$ _____ or _____

5. $3x^2 + 7x + 2 = 0$

$x =$ _____ or _____

6. $2x^2 + 9x + 7 = 0$

$x =$ _____ or _____

7. $x^2 + 12x + 11 = 0$

$x =$ _____ or _____

8. $2x^2 + 13x = -6$

$x =$ _____ or _____

9. $4x^2 + 7x = -3$

$x =$ _____ or _____

10. $x^2 + 13x = -40$

$x =$ _____ or _____

11. $x^2 + 18x + 45 = 0$

$x =$ _____ or _____

12. $2x^2 + 19x + 17 = -13$

$x =$ _____ or _____

The Quadratic Formula with Negative Coefficients

The quadratic equations that you have solved so far have had only positive coefficients. The quadratic formula also works when a quadratic equation has negative coefficients. Be careful to keep track of signs when you are using the formula.

Example 1

Look at the following equation.

$$x^2 - 7x + 6 = 0$$

Step 1. Find the a, b, and c coefficients. Make sure you keep the negative signs with the coefficients.

$$x^2 - 7x + 6 = 0$$

$$a = 1 \qquad b = -7 \qquad c = 6$$

Step 2. Put the coefficients into the quadratic formula. Remember to write the negative signs.

$$x = \frac{-(-7) \pm \sqrt{-7^2 - 4(1)(6)}}{2(1)}$$

Step 3. Do the math inside the square root sign. Then take the square root of the number you find. Remember, a negative number squared is positive.

$$x = \frac{-(-7) \pm \sqrt{49 - 24}}{2(1)} =$$

$$x = \frac{-(-7) \pm \sqrt{25}}{2(1)} =$$

$$x = \frac{-(-7) \pm 5}{2(1)}$$

Step 4. Finish the multiplication. Notice that $-(-7) = 7$.

$$x = \frac{7 \pm 5}{2}$$

Step 5. Because of the plus or minus sign, you will get two
answers.

$$x = \frac{7 + 5}{2} \qquad\qquad x = \frac{7 - 5}{2}$$

$$x = \frac{12}{2} \quad \text{or} \quad x = \frac{2}{2}$$

$$x = 6 \qquad\qquad x = 1$$

The solution is $x = 6$ or $x = 1$.

THINK ABOUT IT

Would you need to use the quadratic formula to
solve the equation $x^2 - 8x + 16 = 0$? Why or why
not? Write your answer on a separate sheet
of paper.

■ PRACTICE 67: The Quadratic Formula with Negative Coefficients

Use the quadratic formula to solve each quadratic equation that
follows. Pay close attention to negative coefficients. You may
need to use another sheet of paper to do the work. Then write
each answer on the line.

1. $2x^2 - 7x + 3 = 0$

$x =$ _____ or _____

2. $3x^2 + 14x - 5 = 0$

$x =$ _____ or _____

3. $2x^2 + 3x = 2$

$x =$ _____ or _____

4. $2x^2 - 11x = -5$

   $x =$ _____ or _____

5. $5x^2 = x + 4$

   $x =$ _____ or _____

6. $2x^2 - 5x - 3 = 0$

   $x =$ _____ or _____

7. $3x^2 + 10x - 25 = 0$

   $x =$ _____ or _____

8. $x^2 + 6x = 7$

   $x =$ _____ or _____

9. $2x^2 - 15x = -25$

   $x =$ _____ or _____

10. $5x^2 = 20x + 25$

   $x =$ _____ or _____

Using the Quadratic Formula to Solve Word Problems

You can use quadratic equations to solve word problems. In some word problems, factors will be obvious. These equations can be solved by factoring. But if the factors are not obvious, it is easier to use the quadratic formula.

Example 1

Read the following problem.

The square of a number is added to 3 times the same number. The total is 28. What is the number? (More than one number may be correct.)

Follow these steps to solve this word problem.

Step 1. Your first step is to translate the word problem into an equation. "The square of a number" can be written as x^2. "Three times the same number" can be written as $3x$. These are being added to each other to equal 28.

$$x^2 + 3x = 28$$

Step 2. Make the equation equal to 0. To do this, subtract 28 from both sides.

$$x^2 + 3x - 28 = 28 - 28$$

$$x^2 + 3x - 28 = 0$$

Step 3. Find the coefficients in the equation.

$$x^2 + 3x - 28 = 0$$

$$a = 1 \qquad b = 3 \qquad c = -28$$

Step 4. Put the coefficients into the quadratic formula.

$$x = \frac{-3 \pm \sqrt{3^2 - 4(1)(-28)}}{2(1)}$$

Step 5. Do the math inside the square root sign. Then take the square root of the number you find. Remember that when you multiply two negative numbers, you get a positive number.

$$x = \frac{-3 \pm \sqrt{9 + 112}}{2(1)}$$

$$x = \frac{-3 \pm \sqrt{121}}{2(1)}$$

$$x = \frac{-3 \pm 11}{2(1)}$$

Step 6. Because of the plus or minus sign, you have two possible answers.

$$x = \frac{-3 + 11}{2} \qquad \text{or} \qquad x = \frac{-3 - 11}{2}$$

$$x = 4 \qquad\qquad\qquad\qquad x = -7$$

THINK ABOUT IT

There is no such thing as the square root of a negative number. Can you explain why this is true? Write your answer on a separate sheet of paper.

Some word problems will ask you to find area or volume. Many of these problems can be solved with quadratic equations.

Look at the example below.

Example 2

The length of a box is one inch longer than twice the width. If the area of the box is 21 square inches, what are the length and width?

Step 1. First you must write the word problem as an equation. Use the formula for finding area: $A = lw$. In this formula, A stands for area, l stands for length, and w stands for width.

You know that the area of the box is 21 square inches. $A = 21$ in². You also know that the length (l) of the box is 1 inch longer than 2 times the (w). This means that $l = 2w + 1$. Now put these terms into the formula.

$$A = lw$$

$$21 = (2w + 1)w$$

$$21 = 2w^2 + w$$

Step 2. Make the equation equal to 0. To do this, subtract 21 from both sides.

$$21 - 21 = 2w^2 + w - 21$$

$$0 = 2w^2 + w - 21$$

Do you recognize this? It is a quadratic equation!

Step 3. Find the coefficients in the equation.

$$0 = 2w^2 + w - 21$$

$$a = 2 \qquad b = 1 \qquad c = -21$$

Step 4. Put the coefficients into the quadratic formula.

$$w = \frac{-1 \pm \sqrt{1^2 - 4(2)(-21)}}{2(2)}$$

Step 5. Do the math inside the square root sign. Then take the square root of the number you find. Remember that when you multiply two negative numbers, the answer is a positive number.

$$w = \frac{-1 \pm \sqrt{1 + 168}}{2(2)}$$

$$w = \frac{-1 \pm \sqrt{169}}{2(2)}$$

$$w = \frac{-1 \pm 13}{2(2)}$$

Step 6. Because of the plus or minus sign, you will end up with two possible answers.

$$w = \frac{-1 + 13}{4} \qquad \text{or} \qquad w = \frac{-1 - 13}{4}$$

$$w = 3 \qquad\qquad\qquad w = -3\,\frac{1}{2}$$

In this word problem, only the positive solution for width (w) makes sense (see "Tip" below). So you know that the width equals 3 inches. But the original word problem asked you to find the width and the length. You know that $l = 2w + 1$ (see step 1). Now put the value for w into this equation to find l.

$$l = 2w + 1$$

$$l = 2(3) + 1$$

$$l = 6 + 1$$

$$l = 7$$

■ **TIP**

When you use quadratic equations, you always end up with two answers, one positive and one negative. But when you are using quadratic equations to solve area or volume problems, you should only use the positive number as your answer.

This makes sense when you think more about it. Imagine what a box looks like. A box cannot have a negative height—it doesn't make sense! Always try to see the shape in the word problem. This will help you to remember when the answer can only be positive.

■ PRACTICE 68: Using the Quadratic Formula to Solve Word Problems

Use the quadratic formula to solve each word problem below. Write each answer on the line.

1. Find the numbers that equal 72 when they are subtracted from their squares.

   _____ and _____

2. The product of two consecutive odd numbers is 255. What are the two numbers?

   _____ and _____

3. The length of a rectangle is 10 inches more than twice its width. The area of the rectangle is 672 square inches. Find the length and width. Use only positive number answers.

   length = _____   width = _____

UNIT 5 REVIEW

Circle the correct answer for each of the following questions or problems.

1. Which of the following is a quadratic equation?
   a. $2x^3 + 3x^2y^3 - 3xy + 2x - 79 = 0$
   b. $x + 5 = 10$
   c. $4x^2 + 8x = -21$
   d. $2x^3 + 2x^2 - 5x + 25 = 0$

2. What are the solutions to the equation $x^2 - 49 = 0$?
   a. $x = 4$ or -4
   b. $x = 49$ or -49
   c. $x = -14$ or 14
   d. $x = -7$ or 7

3. What are the solutions to the equation $x^2 - 6x = -5$?
   a. $x = 5$ or 1
   b. $x = -5$ or -1
   c. $x = -3$ or -2
   d. $x = -3$ or 2

4. What are the solutions to the equation $x^2 + 8x + 12 = -4$?
   a. $x = -4$ only
   b. $x = 4$ only
   c. $x = -4$ or 4
   d. $x = 3$ or -2

5. What are the solutions to the equation $x^2 + 3x - 18 = 0$?
   a. $x = 6$ or -3
   b. $x = -6$ or 3
   c. $x = -9$ or 2
   d. $x = 9$ or -2

6. Using the quadratic formula, find the solutions to this equation: $x^2 + 5x = 0$.
   a. $x = 5$ or 0
   b. $x = -5$ or 0
   c. $x = -3$ or 4
   d. $x = 3$ or -4

7. Which of these equations correctly uses the quadratic formula to solve the equation $5x^2 = x + 4$?

    a. $x = \dfrac{-1 \pm \sqrt{-1 - 80}}{2(5)}$

    b. $x = \dfrac{-4 \pm \sqrt{-5 - 16}}{2(4)}$

    c. $x = \dfrac{-5 \pm \sqrt{16 - 20}}{2(1)}$

    d. $x = \dfrac{1 \pm \sqrt{1 + 80}}{2(5)}$

8. Use the quadratic formula to find the solutions to this equation: $4x^2 = 9x - 2$.

    a. $x = -5\dfrac{3}{4}$ or $-\dfrac{3}{4}$

    b. $x = 4$ or $\dfrac{1}{2}$

    c. $x = 2$ or $\dfrac{1}{4}$

    d. $x = -4$ or $-\dfrac{1}{2}$

9. Using the quadratic formula, find the solutions to this equation: $3x^2 - 2x - 5 = 0$.

    a. $x = 1$ or $-1\dfrac{2}{3}$

    b. $x = -1$ or $1\dfrac{2}{3}$

    c. $x = -\dfrac{3}{5}$ or -1

    d. $x = \dfrac{3}{5}$ or 1

10. Use the quadratic equation to solve the following word problem:

The length of Tom's garden is four feet longer than twice the width. The area of the garden is 30 ft². What are the length and width of Tom's garden? (Remember, the formula for area is $A = lw$.)

   a. $l = 5$ feet; $w = 14$ feet

   b. $l = 14$ feet; $w = 5$ feet

   c. $l = 3$ feet; $w = 10$ feet

   d. $l = 10$ feet; $w = 3$ feet

UNIT 5 APPLICATION ACTIVITY 1

Using Quadratic Equations at Work

You may wonder whether anyone actually uses quadratic equations in real life. Many people do! Two examples of workers who use quadratic equations are architects and engineers. In this activity, you will learn more about how and why these jobs use quadratic equations.

Decide whether you want to learn more about architecture or engineering. Write your choice below:

_____

Now look in the Yellow Pages of your telephone book. If you chose architecture, look for an architectural firm. If you chose engineering, look for an engineering company. Call the company. Tell them you are doing research for a class and you want to learn more about using quadratic equations at work. Ask if there is someone you can speak with for a few minutes. (Remember to be polite and to speak clearly.) Once you have someone on the telephone, ask him or her the questions below. Write the person's answers on the lines provided.

- What is your position? _____

- How do you use quadratic equations at work? _____
_____
_____

- Do you solve quadratic equations with a pencil, a calculator, or a computer? _____

  Why do you solve them this way? _____
_____

- Do you use quadratic equations every day? If not, how often do you use them? _____

- **Optional Activity:** Do some research. Try to find other jobs in which quadratic equations are used. Make a list of all the jobs you can find.

UNIT 5 APPLICATION ACTIVITY 2

Where Did the Quadratic Formula Come From?

You have learned how to use the quadratic formula, but do you know where it came from and who first figured it out? Do some research on the origin of the quadratic formula. Find out who discovered it and why it was needed. In the space below, write a paragraph about what you found out.

_____

_____

_____

_____

_____

_____

_____

_____

_____

_____

_____

_____

_____

_____

_____

_____

_____

APPENDIXES

A. Table of Squares and Square Roots

Number	Square	Positive Square Root
n	n^2	$\sqrt{n}$
1	1	1.00
2	4	1.41
3	9	1.73
4	16	2.00
5	25	2.24
6	36	2.45
7	49	2.65
8	64	2.83
9	81	3.00
10	100	3.16
11	121	3.32
12	144	3.46
13	169	3.61
14	196	3.74
15	225	3.87
16	256	4.00
17	289	4.12
18	324	4.24
19	361	4.36
20	400	4.47
21	441	4.58
22	484	4.69
23	529	4.79
24	576	4.89
25	625	5.00

Number	Square	Positive Square Root
n	n^2	$\sqrt{n}$
26	676	5.09
27	729	5.19
28	784	5.29
29	841	5.39
30	900	5.48
31	961	5.57
32	1024	5.66
33	1089	5.74
34	1156	5.83
35	1225	5.92
36	1296	6.00
37	1369	6.08
38	1444	6.16
39	1521	6.24
40	1600	6.32
41	1681	6.40
42	1764	6.48
43	1849	6.56
44	1936	6.63
45	2025	6.71
46	2116	6.78
47	2209	6.86
48	2304	6.93
49	2401	7.00
50	2500	7.07

Appendixes • Algebra

Number	Square	Positive Square Root
n	n^2	$\sqrt{n}$
51	2601	7.14
52	2704	7.21
53	2809	7.28
54	2916	7.35
55	3025	7.42
56	3136	7.48
57	3249	7.55
58	3364	7.62
59	3481	7.68
60	3600	7.75
61	3721	7.81
62	3844	7.87
63	3969	7.94
64	4096	8.00
65	4225	8.06
66	4356	8.12
67	4489	8.19
68	4624	8.25
69	4761	8.31
70	4900	8.37
71	5041	8.43
72	5184	8.49
73	5329	8.54
74	5476	8.60
75	5625	8.66

Number	Square	Positive Square Root
n	n^2	$\sqrt{n}$
76	5776	8.72
77	5929	8.77
78	6084	8.83
79	6241	8.89
80	6400	8.94
81	6561	9.00
82	6724	9.06
83	6889	9.11
84	7056	9.17
85	7225	9.22
86	7396	9.27
87	7569	9.33
88	7744	9.38
89	7921	9.43
90	8100	9.49
91	8281	9.54
92	8464	9.59
93	8649	9.64
94	8836	9.69
95	9025	9.75
96	9216	9.79
97	9409	9.85
98	9604	9.89
99	9801	9.95
100	10,000	10.00

B. Review of Rules and Formulas

Number Lines
Adding on a Number Line

To add numbers on a number line, look at the second number.

- If it is positive, move to the right.

    Example: (+2) + (+5)

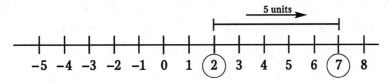

- If it is negative, move to the left.

    Example: (+6) + (−5)

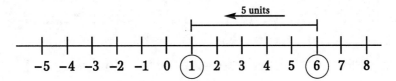

Drawing Number Lines

- To show that a number is included in the solution set, draw a filled-in circle on the number line.

- To show that a number is not included in the solution set, draw an open circle on the number line.

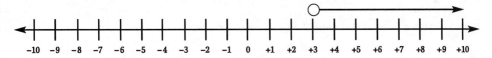

Using Number Lines to Tell Relative Value of Numbers

Use a number line to see the relative value of numbers. Numbers to the left on a number line have smaller values than numbers to the right. This is true whether the numbers are positive or negative.

Example 1: Which has the larger relative value, −2 or 4?

Find both numbers on a number line. The number that is farthest to the right has a greater value than the number that is farthest to the left. In this case, 4 is farther to the right than −2. This means that 4 has a greater value than −2.

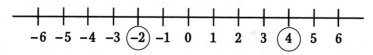

Example 2: Which has the larger relative value, −2 or −4?

Find both numbers on a number line. The number that is farthest to the right has a greater value than the number that is farthest to the left. In this case, −2 is farther to the right than −4. This means that −2 has a greater value than −4.

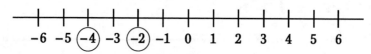

Operations with Signed Numbers
Adding Signed Numbers with the Same Sign

When you add signed numbers that have the same sign, add the absolute values and keep the same sign.

Example 1: $(+6) + (+4) = |6| + |4| = +10$

Example 2: $(-6) + (-4) = |6| + |4| = -10$

Adding Signed Numbers with Different Signs

When you add signed numbers that have different signs, subtract the smaller absolute value from the larger absolute value. Then use the sign of the number with the larger absolute value.

Example: $(-4) + (+6) = |6| - |4| = +2$

Subtracting Signed Numbers

1. Change the sign of the second number.
2. Add the two numbers. Be sure to use the correct addition rule.

Example 1: $(+8) - (+3) = (+8) + (-3) = |8| - |3| = +5$

Example 2: $(+8) - (-3) = (+8) + (+3) = |8| + |3| = +11$

Multiplying and Dividing Signed Numbers with the Same Sign

If the signs of both numbers being multiplied or divided are the same, the answer will be positive.

Example 1: $(+3) \times (+4) = +12$

Example 2: $(-3) \times (-4) = +12$

Example 3: $(+15) \div (+3) = +5$

Example 4: $(-15) \div (-3) = +5$

Multiplying and Dividing Signed Numbers with Different Signs

If the signs of the numbers being multiplied or divided are different, the answer will be negative.

Example 1: $(+3) \times (-4) = -12$

Example 2: $(-3) \times (+4) = -12$

Example 3: $(+15) \div (-3) = -5$

Example 4: $(-15) \div (+3) = -5$

Solving Algebra Equations
Rule 1 for Solving Algebra Equations

You can do anything to an equation as long as you do exactly the same thing to both sides of the equation.

Example: $2x + 3 = 15$

Subtract 1 from both sides, then solve for x:

$2x + 3 - 1 = 15 - 1 \longrightarrow 2x + 2 = 14 \longrightarrow 2x = 12 \longrightarrow x = 6$

Add 7 to both sides, then solve for x:

$2x + 3 + 7 = 15 + 7 \longrightarrow 2x + 10 = 22 \longrightarrow 2x = 12 \longrightarrow x = 6$

Multiply both sides by 4, then solve for x:

$4(2x + 3) = 4(15) \longrightarrow 8x + 12 = 60 \longrightarrow 8x = 48 \longrightarrow x = 6$

Divide both sides by 2, then solve for x:

$$\frac{2x + 3}{2} = \frac{15}{2} \longrightarrow x + 1\frac{1}{2} = 7\frac{1}{2} \longrightarrow x = 6$$

Rule 2 for Solving Algebra Equations

To find the value of an unknown number

1. Combine any like terms.
2. Do the opposite of what has been done to the variable to both sides of the equation.

Example: $7x + 5 - 4x = 17$

1. Combine any like terms.
$$(7x - 4x) + (5 - 5) = (17 - 5)$$
$$3x = 12$$

2. Do the opposite of what has been done to the variable to both sides of the equation. In this case, the variable is being multiplied by 3, so you divide both sides by 3.

$$\frac{3x}{3} = \frac{12}{3}$$

$$x = 4$$

Solving Two-Step Equations Without Parentheses

When there are no parentheses but there is more than one operation

1. Add or subtract, if necessary, to get all the variables on one side of the equation and any constants on the other side.
2. If the variable has a coefficient other than 1, multiply or divide both sides of the equation to get x by itself.

Example: $4x - 8 = 12$

1. Add or subtract to get all the variables on one side and any constants on the other side. In this case, add 8 to both sides.

$$4x - 8 + 8 = 12 + 8$$

$$4x = 20$$

2. If the variable has a coefficient other than 1, see what operation is being done to the variable. Then use the inverse operation on both sides of the equation. In this case, the variable is being multiplied by 4. To get a value for x alone, divide both sides of the equation by 4.

$$\frac{4x}{4} = \frac{20}{4}$$

$$x = 5$$

Solving Two-Step Equations with Parentheses

If an equation includes terms in parentheses

1. Multiply the terms inside the parentheses by the terms just outside the parentheses.
2. Collect like terms.
3. Add or subtract, if necessary, to get all the variables on one side of the equation and any constants on the other side.
4. If the variable has a coefficient other than 1, multiply or divide both sides of the equation to get x by itself. (Remember, an equation remains true as long as you do the same thing to both sides.)

Example: $2(x-5) + 6x = 14$

1. Multiply the terms inside the parentheses by the terms just outside the parentheses.

   $$2(x) - 2(5) + 6x = 14$$

   $$2x - 10 + 6x = 14$$

2. Collect like terms.

   $$(2x + 6x) - 10 = 14$$

   $$8x - 10 = 14$$

3. Move all the variables to one side and all the constants to the other side by adding or subtracting on both sides of the equation. In this case, add 10 to both sides of the equation.

   $$8x - 10 + 10 = 14 + 10$$

   $$8x = 24$$

4. If the variable has a coefficient other than 1, see what operation is being done to the variable. Then use the

inverse operation on both sides of the equation. In this case, the variable is being multiplied by 8. To get a value for x alone, divide both sides of the equation by 8.

$$\frac{8x}{8} = \frac{24}{8}$$

$$x = 3$$

Solving Equations with Fractional Coefficients

If the coefficient of the variable is a fraction, change it to a whole number. To do this, multiply both sides of the equation by the reciprocal of the fraction—the number that, when multiplied by the fraction, gives a product of 1. To find the reciprocal, switch the numerator and the denominator of the fraction.

Example: $\frac{2}{3}x = 12$

1. Find the reciprocal of the fraction by switching the numerator and the denominator. In this case, the reciprocal of $\frac{2}{3}$ is $\frac{3}{2}$.

$$\frac{2}{3} \bullet \frac{3}{2} = \frac{6}{6} = 1$$

2. Multiply both sides of the equation by the reciprocal.

$$\frac{3}{2}\left(\frac{2}{3}x\right) = \frac{3}{2}(12)$$

$$x = \frac{36}{2}$$

$$x = 18$$

Solving Equations with Squared Variables

Some equations include squared variables. To solve the equation, you need to get x by itself.

1. Find a value of the variable without a reciprocal. See what operation is being done to the variable. Then use the inverse operation on both sides of the equation.
2. Take the square root of both sides of the equation. The exponent of the variable shows how many times the variable has been used as a factor. x^2 uses x as a factor twice; it is the same as $x \cdot x$. x^3 uses x as a factor three times; it is the same as $x \cdot x \cdot x$. Use a calculator with a square root key, or the Table of Squares and Square Roots on pages 257–260, to find the square root of a constant number.

Example: $3x^2 = 48$

1. Use inverse operations on both sides of the equation to find a value of x without a reciprocal. In this case, divide both sides of the equation by 3.

$$\frac{3x^2}{3} = \frac{48}{3} \longrightarrow x^2 = 16$$

2. Take the square root of both sides of the equation. Since x^2 is the same as $x \cdot x$, we know that the square root of x^2 is x. Use a calculator or a square root table to find the square root of the constant. In this case, the square root of 16 is 4; $4 \cdot 4 = 16$.

$$\sqrt{x^2} = \sqrt{16} \longrightarrow x = 4$$

Equations That Equal Zero

The only number that can be multiplied by another number to have a product of 0 is 0. Because of this, if an equation is equal to 0 and the known number is not 0, then the unknown number must be 0.

Example: $y \cdot 12 = 0$

The only number that can be multiplied by 12 for a product of 0 is 0. Therefore, $y = 0$.

Working with Inequalities
Rule 1 for Inequalities: Adding and Subtracting

You can add or subtract the same number to or from each side of an inequality and it will still be true.

Example: $7 > 3$

$$7 + 2 > 3 + 2 \qquad \longrightarrow \qquad 9 > 5$$

$$7 - 2 > 3 - 2 \qquad \longrightarrow \qquad 5 > 1$$

Rule 2 for Inequalities: Multiplying and Dividing with Positive Numbers

You can multiply or divide each side of an inequality by the same positive number and the inequality will still be true.

Example: $6 > 4$

$$6(4) > 4(4) \qquad \longrightarrow \qquad 24 > 16$$

$$\frac{6}{2} > \frac{4}{2} \qquad \longrightarrow \qquad 3 > 2$$

Rule 3 for Inequalities: Multiplying and Dividing with Negative Numbers

You can multiply or divide each side of an inequality by the same negative number, but in order for the inequality to remain true, you must change the direction of the inequality sign.

Example: $5 < 7$

1. Multiply both sides by –4.

   $5(-4) \longrightarrow -20$

   $7(-4) \longrightarrow -28$

   The inequality is no longer true; –20 is not less than –28.

2. Change the direction of the inequality sign.

   $5(-4) > 7(-4) \longrightarrow -20 > -28$

   The new inequality is true. –20 is greater than –28.

Graphing Linear Equations
The Table Method

To show linear equations on the coordinate plane, make a table of values for the variables in the equation. Once you have several values for both x and y, write them as ordered pairs. Then graph the ordered pairs on the coordinate plane.

Example: $3x + y = 2$

1. Set up a table. Write x above one column and y above the other.

x	y

2. Choose several values for x. You can choose any values for x, but it is usually easiest to work with small whole numbers. Try working with –1, 0, and 1 as values for x. Write these values in the table under the x.

x	y
–1	
0	
1	

3. For each value of x, find the corresponding value of y. To do this, substitute each value for x in the equation. Start with $x = -1$.

$$3x + y = 2$$

$$3(-1) + y = 2$$

$$-3 + y = 2$$

4. Get y by itself on one side of the equation. In this case, add 3 to both sides.

$$(-3 + 3) + y = 2 + 3$$

$$y = 5$$

5. Now you know that when $x = -1$, $y = 5$. Write 5 in the table under y, on the same row as –1.

x	y
–1	5
0	
1	

6. Do the same for the other values of *x* in the table.

           $x = 0$ $x = 1$

           $3(0) + y = 2$ $3(1) + y = 2$

           $0 + y = 2$ $(3 - 3) + y = 2 - 3$

           $y = 2$ $y = -1$

7. Write each value for *y* in the table.

X	y
−1	5
0	2
1	−1

8. Write the values in the table as ordered pairs. The *x*-values will be the *x*-coordinates. The *y*-values will be the *y*-coordinates.

        (−1, 5), (0, 2), (1, −1)

9. Graph the ordered pairs on a coordinate plane. Draw a straight line that connects all three of the points.

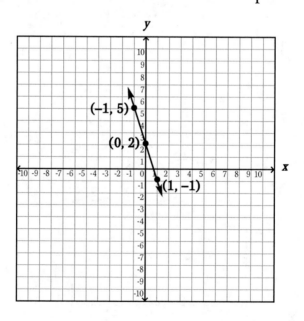

The Intercept Method

You can graph a linear equation by drawing a line using only two points on the coordinate plane—the two points where the line of the linear equation meets (intersects with) the axes of the coordinate plane.

First, find the two points where the line of the linear equation intersects with the axes of the coordinate plane. To do this, you must find the value for y when x equals 0. You must also find the value for x when y equals 0. Then make your solution into ordered pairs, graph the points on the coordinate plane, and draw a straight line through the points.

Example: $-2x + y = 4$

1. Find the value for y when x equals 0 by substituting 0 for x.

   $-2(0) + y = 4$

   $0 + y = 4$

   $y = 4$

2. Now, find the value for x when y equals 0. To do this, start by substituting 0 for y.

   $-2x + 0 = 4$

   $-2x = 4$

3. Divide both sides by -2 to get x by itself on one side of the equation.

   $$\frac{-2x}{-2} = \frac{4}{-2}$$

   $x = -2$

4. Make your solutions into ordered pairs. The *x* value is the *x*-coordinate. The *y* value is the *y*-coordinate.

    (−2, 0)

    (0, 4)

5. Graph the two points on the coordinate plane. Draw a straight line that goes through both of them.

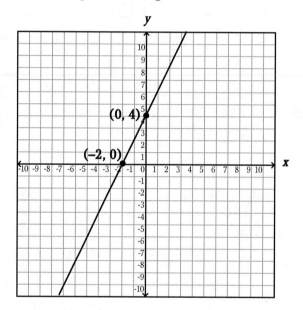

Slope
The Formula for Finding Slope

m = slope of a line

$y1$ = *y*-coordinate of the first point on a line

$y2$ = *y*-coordinate of the second point on a line

$x1$ = *x*-coordinate of the first point on a line

$x2$ = *x*-coordinate of the second point on a line

$$m = \frac{(y2 - y1)}{(x2 - x1)}$$

Positive and Negative Slope

If a line moves up as it goes from left to right across the page, it has a positive slope. If a line moves down as it goes from left to right across the page, it has a negative slope. Line A in the diagram below has a positive slope. Line B in the diagram below has a negative slope.

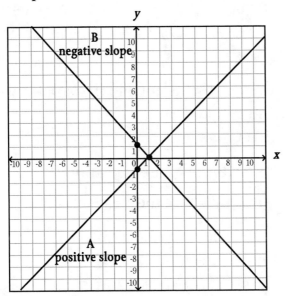

Working with Polynomials
Ordering Polynomials

Some polynomials have terms with the same variable to different powers. In that case, the terms should be written so the powers are in decreasing order.

Example: $3x^2 + 2x + 3$

Multiplying Terms with the Same Variable

To multiply two terms that have the same variable

1. Multiply the coefficients of the terms.
2. Add the exponents.

3. Multiply the results from steps 1 and 2.

Example: $(5x^3)(3x^2)$

1. Multiply the coefficients of the two terms. This gives you the coefficient of the new term.
$$5 \cdot 3 = 15$$

2. Add the exponents of the variables in both terms. This gives you the exponent of the variable in the new term.
$$(x^3)(x^2) \quad \longrightarrow \quad x^{3+2} \quad \longrightarrow \quad x^5$$

3. Multiply the new coefficient and the variable with the new exponent (steps 1 and 2).
$$(15)(x^5) = 15x^5$$

Dividing Terms with the Same Variable

To divide two terms that have the same variable:

1. Divide the coefficients of the terms.
2. Subtract the exponents.
3. Multiply the results of steps 1 and 2.

Example: $\dfrac{15x^5}{3x^3}$

1. Divide the coefficients of the two terms. This gives you the coefficient of the new term.
$$\frac{15}{3} = 5$$

2. Subtract the exponent of the divisor (the term "dividing into"—the term below the line) from the exponent of the dividend (the term being divided—the term above the line). This gives you the exponent of the variable in the new term.

$$\frac{x^5}{x^3} \longrightarrow x^{3-2} \longrightarrow x^2$$

3. Multiply the new coefficient and the variable with the new exponent (steps 1 and 2).

$$(5)(x^5) = 5x^2$$

Multiplying Binomials

To multiply two binomials, multiply both terms of one binomial by both terms of the other binomial. Use the FOIL Method to make sure you don't miss any terms: First, Outer, Inner, Last.

Example: $(5x + 4)(7x + 3)$

1. Multiply the first terms of both binomials.

$$5x \bullet 7x = 35x^2$$

2. Multiply the outer terms of both binomials.

$$5x \bullet 3 = 15x$$

3. Multiply the inner terms of both binomials.

$$4 \bullet 7x = 28x$$

4. Multiply the last terms of both binomials.

$$4 \bullet 3 = 12$$

5. Add the results of the first four steps.

$$35x^2 + 15x + 28x + 12$$

6. Combine like terms.

$$35x^2 + (15x + 28x) + 12 \longrightarrow 35x^2 + 43x + 12$$

$$(5x + 4)(7x + 3) = 35x^2 + 43x + 12$$

Multiplying Special Binomials with the Form $(x + y) \bullet (x - y)$

When you multiply two binomials with the form $(x + y)(x - y)$, the answer is always $x^2 - y^2$. Rather than multiply the terms, you can just use this rule:

$$(x + y)(x - y) = x^2 - y^2$$

Example: $(5x + 4)(5x - 4) = (5x)^2 - (4)^2 = 25x^2 - 16$

Factoring

What Numbers Can Be Used as Factors?

Any numbers that, when multiplied, give a certain product can be used as factors of that product.

Example 1: factors of 10

$$1 \bullet 10 = 10$$

$$2 \bullet 5 = 10$$

$$-1 \bullet -10 = 10$$

$$-2 \bullet -5 = 10$$

Any of these pairs can be used as factors of 10.

Example 2: factors of $4y$

$$4 \bullet y = 4y$$

$$2 \bullet 2y = 4y$$

$$-4 \bullet -y = 4y$$

$$-2 \bullet -2y = 4y$$

$$-2 \bullet 2 \bullet -y = 4y$$

$$-2 \bullet -2 \bullet y = 4y$$

Any of these groups can be used as factors of $4y$.

Factoring Trinomials

Rule 1

- If the second and third terms of a trinomial are positive, then the last term in each binomial factor will also be positive. In other words, $x^2 + bx + c = (x + ?)(x + ?)$.

Example: $y^2 + 7y + 12 = (y + 3)(y + 4)$

Rule 2

- If the second term of a trinomial is negative and the third term is positive, then the last term in each binomial factor will be negative. In other words, $x^2 - bx + c = (x - ?)(x - ?)$.

Example: $y^2 + 9y + 18 = (y - 6)(y - 3)$

Rule 3

- If the third term of a trinomial is negative, then the last term in one binomial factor will be negative, and the last term in the other binomial factor will be positive.

Example: $y^2 - 2y - 15 = (y - 3)(y + 5)$

$x^2 + 9x - 22 = (x - 2)(x + 11)$

Rule 4

- When you multiply the last terms in the binomial factors of a trinomial, the product must be the last term in the trinomial. These terms must also add up to the coefficient of the trinomial's second term.

Example: $y^2 + 7y + 12 = (y + ?)(y + ?)$

1. The last terms in the binomials must have both a product of 12 and a sum of 7. Factors that have a product of 12 include

1, 12	−1, −12
2, 6	−2, −6
3, 4	−3, −4

2. From this list of possible factors, the only ones that have a sum of 7 are 3, 4. Therefore, the last terms in the binomial factors must be 3 and 4.

$$y^2 + 7y + 12 = (y + 3)(y + 4)$$

Quadratic Equations

What Is a Quadratic Equation?

A quadratic equation is an equation that

1. uses only one variable
2. has at least one term with an exponent of 2
3. has no exponents higher than 2

Example: $y^2 + 7y + 12 = 0$

Factoring Quadratic Equations

Many quadratic equations can be solved by factoring. The factors of equations that can be solved by factoring follow certain patterns.

- If the second and third terms of the trinomial are positive, the last term in both binomial factors will be positive.

- If the second term of the trinomial is negative and the third term is positive, the last term in both binomial factors will be negative.

- If the second term of the trinomial is positive and the third term is negative, the last term in one binomial factor will be positive and the other will be negative.
- If the second and third terms of the trinomial are both negative, the last term in one binomial factor will be positive and the other will be negative.

Equation	Binomial Factors
$x^2 + bx + c = 0$	$(x+?)(x+?) = 0$
$x^2 - bx + c = 0$	$(x-?)(x-?) = 0$
$x^2 + bx - c = 0$	$(x+?)(x-?) = 0$
$x^2 - bx - c = 0$	$(x+?)(x-?) = 0$

The Quadratic Formula

This formula can be used to solve quadratic equations in the form $ax^2 + bx + c = 0$. Where x is the variable, a is the coefficient of the first term in the equation, b is the coefficient of the second term, and c is the constant, then:

$$x = \frac{-b \pm \sqrt{b^2 - 4ac}}{2a}$$

To solve a quadratic equation using this formula

1. Make sure the equation is in the proper form. If the equation is not equal to 0, add or subtract from both sides until it equals 0.
2. Find the values of a, b, and c in the equation. Write the values in the formula in place of the letters.

3. Do the math to solve the equation. Because it includes the sign ±, which means "plus or minus," this formula always gives you two solutions.

Example: $2x^2 + 7x = -3$

1. Make sure the equation is in the proper form, equal to 0. In this case, add 3 to both sides of the equation.

$$2x^2 + 7x + 3 = -3 + 3$$

$$2x^2 + 7x + 3 = 0$$

2. Find the values of a, b, and c, and write them in the formula in place of the letters.

$$a = 2,\ b = 7,\ c = 3$$

$$x = \frac{-7 \pm \sqrt{7^2 - 4(2 \cdot 3)}}{2 \cdot 2}$$

3. Do the math, step by step, to solve the equation.

$$x = \frac{-7 \pm \sqrt{49 - 24}}{4}$$

$$x = \frac{-7 \pm \sqrt{25}}{4}$$

$$x = \frac{-7 \pm 5}{4}$$

$$x = \frac{-7 + 5}{4} \quad \text{or} \quad x = \frac{-7 - 5}{4}$$

$$x = -\frac{2}{4} \quad \text{or} \quad x = -\frac{12}{4}$$

$$x = -\frac{1}{2} \quad \text{or} \quad x = -3$$

4. The two possible solutions for x are $-\dfrac{1}{2}$ and -3.

Signs and Symbols

Symbol	Meaning	Example
•	multiply by	$7 \cdot 4 = 28$
( )	multiply by	$7(4) = 28$
$\neq$	is not equal to	$3 \neq 4$
$<$	is less than	$3 < 4$
$>$	is greater than	$4 > 3$
$\leq$	is less than or equal to	$3 \leq 4, 3 \leq 3$
$\geq$	is greater than or equal to	$4 \geq 3, 4 \geq 4$
$=$	is equal to	$3 + 1 = 4$
$\pm$	plus or minus	$x \pm 4$
$\sqrt{}$	the square root of	$\sqrt{9} = 3$
| |	absolute value	$|-5| = 5$

Formulas
The Distance Formula

This formula can be used to find distance traveled, rate traveled, or time traveled.

distance = rate times time: $D = rt$

rate = distance divided by time: $\dfrac{D}{t} = r$

time = distance divided by rate: $\dfrac{D}{r} = t$

The Quadratic Formula

This formula can be used to solve quadratic equations. Where x is the variable, a is the coefficient of the first term in the equation, b is the coefficient of the second term, and c is the constant, then

$$x = \frac{-b \pm \sqrt{b^2 - 4ac}}{2a}$$

Area of a Rectangle

Where A stands for the area of a rectangle, l stands for the length of the rectangle, and w stands for the width of the rectangle, then

$$A = lw$$

GLOSSARY

absolute value (AB-suh-loot VAL-yoo) the distance of a number from zero on a number line; written as $|x|$

actual value (AK-chuh-wul VAL-yoo) what a number is really worth, as opposed to its absolute value

algebraic expression (al-juh-BRAY-ik ik-SPRE-shun) an expression that includes at least one variable, such as $x + 8$

axes (AK-seez) the horizontal number line (x-axis) and vertical number line (y-axis) on a coordinate plane; the singular is "axis."

axis (AK-sus) either of the number lines (horizontal and vertical) used to form a coordinate plane; the plural is "axes."

binomial (by-NOH-mee-ul) a polynomial with two terms that are separated by an addition or a subtraction sign, such as $4x - 7$

coefficient (koh-uh-FI-shunt) a constant that multiplies a variable; for example, in $9x$, 9 is the coefficient of x.

combining like terms (kum-BYN-ing LYK TURMZ) adding or subtracting like terms—numbers with the same variable and the same exponent—to make an expression shorter

common factor (KO-mun FAK-tur) a number that is a factor of two or more numbers

complete factoring (kum-PLEET FAK-tuh-ring) breaking an expression into its factors so that it cannot be factored any further

constant (KON-stunt) a term that has no variable; the value remains constant.

coordinates (koh-ORD-nuts) a pair of numbers used to locate a point on a coordinate plane

coordinate plane (koh-ORD-nut PLAYN) a flat surface divided into four parts by a horizontal line (x-axis) and a vertical line (y-axis) that meet in the center of the plane

cubed (KYOOBD) multiplied by itself, then by itself again; shown with the exponent 3, as in 4^3, or $(4 \cdot 4 \cdot 4)$

denominator (di-NO-muh-nay-tur) the number on the bottom of a fraction

difference (DI-furns) the answer in a subtraction problem

difference between two squares (DI-furns bi-TWEEN TOO SKWAYRZ) a binomial in which both terms are perfect squares and one term is negative

distance formula (DIS-tuns FOR-myuh-luh) a general rule for finding the distance covered, if you know the rate and time traveled. Distance = (rate)(time), or $D = rt$.

dividend (DI-vuh-dend) in a division problem, the number that is to be divided by the other number; in $42 \div 6$, the dividend is 42.

divisor (duh-VY-zur) in a division problem, the number that divides the dividend; in $42 \div 6$, the divisor is 6.

equation (i-KWAY-zhun) a number sentence that says that one expression is equal to another; formed by placing an equal sign between the two expressions. Equations may include variables, as in $3 - n = 10$.

exponent (ik-SPOH-nunt) a small, raised number that shows repeated multiplication of the same factor. The number in the exponent shows how many times the number is used as a factor, such as 5^3, in which 5 is used as a factor 3 times: $5 \cdot 5 \cdot 5$.

expression (ik-SPRE-shun) a mathematical phrase that combines operations, numbers, and/or variables

---

PRONUNCIATION KEY

CAPITAL LETTERS show the stressed syllables.

a	as in m**a**t	f	as in **f**it
ay	as in d**ay**, s**ay**	g	as in **g**o
ch	as in **ch**ew	i	as in s**i**t
e	as in b**e**d	j	as in **j**ob, **g**em
ee	as in **e**v**e**n, **ea**sy, n**ee**d	k	as in **c**ool, **k**ey

factor (FAK-tur) a number that is multiplied by another number to get a product

factoring (FAK-tuh-ring) finding the numbers, or factors, that can be multiplied to give a certain product

FOIL method (FOYL ME-thud) rule for multiplying terms in binomials; the letters stand for first terms, outside terms, inside terms, last terms.

formula (FOR-myuh-luh) a general rule for finding the value of something; often written with variables

greatest common factor (GCF) (GRAYT-ust KO-mun FAK-tur) the largest number that will divide evenly into two or more numbers

horizontal (hor-uh-ZON-tul) going from side to side

inequality (i-ni-KWO-luh-tee) a mathematical statement that says that two expressions may not be equal; formed by placing an inequality symbol ($\neq, >, <, \geq, \leq$) between the expressions

inequality symbol (i-ni-KWO-luh-tee SIM-bul) symbol that shows that two expressions may not be equal

intercept method (IN-tur-sept ME-thud) graphing a linear equation by connecting the two points where the line meets the axes of the coordinate plane

intersect (in-tur-SEKT) to cross at exactly one point

inverse operation (IN-vurs o-puh-RAY-shun) operation that is the inverse, or opposite, of another operation, and undoes the action of that operation. Addition and subtraction are inverse operations; multiplication and division are inverse operations.

PRONUNCIATION KEY

CAPITAL LETTERS show the stressed syllables.

ng	as in runni**ng**	u	as in b**u**t, s**o**me
o	as in c**o**t, f**a**ther	uh	as in **a**bout, tak**e**n, lem**o**n,
oh	as in g**o**, n**o**te		pen**ci**l
sh	as in **sh**y	ur	as in t**er**m
th	as in **th**in	y	as in l**i**ne, fl**y**
oo	as in t**oo**	zh	as in vi**s**ion, mea**s**ure

287

Glossary • Algebra

like monomials (LYK mo-NOH-mee-ulz) monomials that have the same variable and the same exponent

like terms (LYK TURMZ) terms that have the same variable and the same exponent; in the algebraic expression $3y^2 + 6y + 2y + 4$, the like terms are $6y$ and $2y$.

line (LYN) a straight path that goes on forever in two different directions

linear equations (LI-nee-ur i-KWAY-zhunz) equations that have to do with lines

monomial (mo-NOH-mee-ul) a polynomial with only one term, such as $4x$

negative number (NE-guh-tiv NUM-bur) a number with a value of less than zero; the opposite of a positive number

numerator (NOO-muh-ray-tur) the number on the top of a fraction

operation (o-puh-RAY-shun) a mathematical process, such as addition, subtraction, multiplication, or division

ordered pair (OR-durd PAYR) a pair of numbers used to locate a point on a coordinate plane, usually written inside parentheses; the first number tells how far to move horizontally and the second number tells how far to move vertically.

ordering polynomials (OR-dur-ing po-luh-NOH-mee-uls) writing polynomials so that the term with the largest exponent comes first, followed by the next-largest exponent, and so on, such as $3y^3 + 6y^2 + 2y + 4$

origin (OR-uh-jun) the point at which the x-axis and the y-axis in the coordinate plane intersect

---

PRONUNCIATION KEY

CAPITAL LETTERS show the stressed syllables.

a	as in m**a**t	f	as in **f**it
ay	as in d**ay**, s**ay**	g	as in **g**o
ch	as in **ch**ew	i	as in s**i**t
e	as in b**e**d	j	as in **j**ob, **g**em
ee	as in **e**v**e**n, **ea**sy, n**ee**d	k	as in **c**ool, **k**ey

parentheses (puh-REN-thuh-seez) a pair of curved marks ( ) with two uses in algebra. Parentheses are used to show that the number or numbers inside the parentheses should be multiplied by the number outside the parentheses, for example, $3(2 + 4)$. They are also used to separate mathematical expressions, for example, $(2 + 3) - (1 + 1)$.

perfect square quadratic equation (PUR-fikt SKWAYR kwa-DRA-tik i-KWAY-zhun) a quadratic equation that is the square of a single binomial, for example, $4x^2 + 8x + 4 = 0$ is the square of $2x + 2 = 0$.

polynomial (pol-uh-NOH-mee-ul) an expression with one or more terms, separated by plus or minus signs, such as $6x + 5$

positive number (PO-zuh-tiv NUM-bur) a number with a value of more than zero; the opposite of a negative number. It may or may not be indicated with a plus sign (+).

power (POW-ur) a small, raised number that shows repeated multiplication of the same factor

product (PRO-dukt) the answer to a multiplication problem

property (PRO-pur-tee) a statement that has either been proved to be true, or can be assumed to be true

quadratic equation (kwah-DRA-tik i-KWAY-zhun) an equation that has at least one term with a power of 2, has no terms with a power of more than 2, and uses only one variable; $3x^2 + 2x + 3 = 0$ is an example of a quadratic equation.

PRONUNCIATION KEY

CAPITAL LETTERS show the stressed syllables.

ng as in runni**ng**	u as in b**u**t, s**o**me
o as in c**o**t, f**a**ther	uh as in **a**bout, tak**e**n, lem**o**n, penc**i**l
oh as in g**o**, n**o**te	
sh as in **sh**y	ur as in t**er**m
th as in **th**in	y as in l**i**ne, fl**y**
oo as in t**oo**	zh as in vi**s**ion, mea**s**ure

quadratic formula (kwah-DRA-tik FOR-myuh-luh) formula used to solve quadratic equations; where x is the variable, a is the coefficient of the first term in the equation, b is the coefficient of the second term, and c is the constant, then:

$$x = \frac{-b \pm \sqrt{b^2 - 4ac}}{2a}$$

ratio (RAY-shee-oh) the relationship between two numbers showing how they compare to each other

reciprocal (ri-SI-pruh-kul) one of two numbers whose product is 1; the reciprocal of any number x is $\frac{1}{x}$. For example, 7 and $\frac{1}{7}$ are reciprocals of each other, since $7 \cdot \frac{1}{7} = 1$.

signed number (SYND NUM-bur) a positive or negative number; its value in relation to zero can be shown by a plus (+) or minus (−) sign.

simplify (SIM-pluh-fy) collect like terms

single term (SING-gul TURM) an algebraic expression that consists of only one term, with no plus, minus, or multiplication sign; for example, $4y$ is a single term.

slope (SLOHP) the steepness of the slant of a line

solution (suh-LOO-shun) the value for a variable that makes an equation true

solve (SOLV) to find the value of the variable that makes a number sentence true

---

PRONUNCIATION KEY

CAPITAL LETTERS show the stressed syllables.

a	as in m**a**t	f	as in **f**it
ay	as in d**ay**, s**ay**	g	as in **g**o
ch	as in **ch**ew	i	as in s**i**t
e	as in b**e**d	j	as in **j**ob, **g**em
ee	as in **e**ven, **ea**sy, n**ee**d	k	as in **c**ool, **k**ey

special binomials (SPE-shul by-NOH-mee-ulz) pairs of binomials that take the form $(a + b)(a - b)$; $(2x + 3)(2x - 3)$ is an example of a special binomial.

square root (SKWAYR ROOT) the square root of a number is the factor that, when multiplied by itself, gives the number. The symbol for "square root of" is $\sqrt{}$, as in $\sqrt{9} = 3$.

squared (SKWAYRD) multiplied by itself; can be shown with the exponent 2, as in 3^2, or $3 \bullet 3$

squared variable (SKWAYRD VER-ee-uh-bul) a variable that is multiplied by itself, shown with the exponent 2, as in x^2, or $x \bullet x$

subtrahend (SUB-truh-hend) in a subtraction problem, the number to be subtracted, or taken away, to find the difference between the two numbers; in $7 - 5$, the subtrahend is 5.

sum (SUM) the answer to an addition problem

term (TURM) a number, a variable, or a combination of numbers and variables

trinomial (try-NOH-mee-ul) a polynomial with three terms, separated by addition or subtraction signs; $7a + 4b - 8$ is an example of a trinomial.

unknown number (un-NOHN NUM-bur) a number whose value is not known

variable (VER-ee-uh-bul) a letter or other symbol that represents a number. A variable does not always represent one specific number; its value can change, or vary.

PRONUNCIATION KEY

CAPITAL LETTERS show the stressed syllables.

ng as in running	u as in but, some
o as in cot, father	uh as in about, taken, lemon, pencil
oh as in go, note	
sh as in shy	ur as in term
th as in thin	y as in line, fly
oo as in too	zh as in vision, measure

vertical (VUR-ti-kul) going up and down

x-axis (EKS AK-sus) the horizontal number line on a coordinate plane

x-coordinate (EKS koh-ORD-nut) the first number in an ordered pair that tells how far to move left or right from the origin

y-axis (WY AK-sus) the vertical (up-and-down) number line on a coordinate plane

y-coordinate (WY koh-ORD-nut) the second number in an ordered pair that tells how far to move up or down from the origin

INDEX

absolute values, 8–9
  symbol for, 10
actual values, 8–9
addition
  first rule for, 14–16
  of like terms, 149–151
  of polynomials, 155–158
  of positive and negative
    numbers, 11–14
  second rule for, 17–19
  of signed numbers, 15, 17,
    262–263
  solving equations with, 57–58
algebra. *See also* algebraic equations
  algebraic equations, 36–38
  algebraic expressions, 29
  applying, to fund-raising, 210–211
  figuring out credit card charges
    using, 106–107
  finding values of unknown
    numbers with, 25
  planning a party using, 208–210
  solving word problems in, 46
    without formulas, 81
algebraic equations, 36–38. *See also*
  equations
  changing word problems to, 52–53
  setting up, 81–83
  that equal zero, 218–219
algebraic expressions. *See also*
  expressions
  definition of, 29
  examples of, 29

binomials, 154
  definition of, 224
  multiplying, 172–173, 277
    using FOIL method, 174–175

  solving special binomial quadratic
    equations, 221–224
  special. *See* special binomials
Boole, George, 51

calculators, 242
coefficients, 26
  adding and subtracting, 151
  placement of, 217
  quadratic formula with
    negative, 244–245
  solving equations with
    fractional, 67–68, 267
combining like terms, 31–35, 64–66
  paying attention to signs
    when, 33–34
common factor, 184
complete factoring, 204–206
constant terms, 64
coordinate planes
  forming, 112
  graphing lines on, 116–121
  graphing points in, 113–115
  origin of, 113
  x and y axes on, 113
coordinates, 114
  finding, 123–125
  using, to find things on maps, 145
credit cards
  figuring purchases made
    with, 106–107
cubed, 70

denominator, 67
  canceling out like variables in, 166
difference, 165
difference between two squares,
  187–189
Diophantus, 51

distance formula, 77, 283
    for finding out lengths of trips, 80
        examples for, 105–106
    problems using, 78–80
distributive property, 198
dividend, 26
division
    difference between factoring
      and, 179
    of monomials, 167–169
    to show, 26
    of signed numbers, 22–24
        with different signs, 23, 263
        with the same sign, 23, 263
    solving equations with, 59–60
    of terms with same
      variable, 276–277
    of variables with
      exponents, 164–166
divisor, 26

equal sign, 36, 84
    definition of, 38
equations, 36–38. *See also* algebraic
  equations
    doing same thing to both sides
      of, 37, 264
    with fractional coefficients,
      solving, 67–68, 267
    linear. *See* linear equations
    with parentheses, 72–76
    quadratic. *See* quadratic equations
    solving
      by dividing and multiplying,
        59–60
      by subtracting and adding,
        57–58
    with squared variables,
      solving, 69–71

that equal zero, 269
two-step, solving, 61–63
    with parentheses, 266–267
    rule for, 62
    without parentheses, 265–266
with variables, 39–41
exponents, 69, 70. *See also* powers
  adding, 161
  dividing variables with, 164–166
  multiplying variables
    with, 160–161
  in quadratic equations, 215
expressions
  definition of, 29
  dividing monomials to
    simplify, 168
  solving, 29–30

factoring, 179–182
  complete, 204–206
  definition of, 180
  difference between division
    and, 179
  methods of, 204
  quadratic equations, 229–230,
    280–281
    four types of, 230, 231–235
  trinomials, 190–192, 279–280
    first rule for, 192
    more difficult, 199–204
    with negative terms, 193–195
    other negative, 196–198
    second rule for, 195
    third rule for, 198
  useful aspects of, 181, 182
factors, 179
  finding, 182–183
  numbers that can be used as, 278
FOIL method, 174–175

multiplying terms inside, 76
placing like terms in, 155
to show multiplication, 26
solving two-step equations
  with, 266–267
  without, 265
using, for ordered pairs, 114
percentages, 52–53
perfect square quadratic equations,
  225–227
plus sign, 4, 76
point(s)
  easiest, to find coordinates
    for, 123–125
  graphing a line when you know
    slope and one, 138–141
  graphing, in coordinate
    planes, 113–115
  represented by ordered pairs,
    graphing, 114–115
polynomials. *See also* ordering
  polynomials
  adding and subtracting, 155–158
  arranging terms in, 153
  definition of, 152
  multiplying monomials
    by, 170–171
  placing, in correct order, 220
  that have two terms. *See* binomials
positive numbers, 3–4
  adding negative and, 11–14
  on number line, 7
  subtracting negative and, 20–21
  on vertical number line, 111
positive sign. *See* plus sign
powers, 153. *See also* exponents
problems, algebra
  checking answers for, 42–43, 58
  rule 1 for solving, 37
  rule 2 for solving, 39–41

product(s)
  definition of, 160
  finding exponent of, 160
  of two special binomials, 177
  zero, 218–219
property, 198

quadratic equations, 215–216
  changing, to equal zero, 219–220
  components of, 215, 280
  exponents in, 215
  factoring, 280–281
  solved by factoring, 229–230
    four types of, 230, 231–235
  solving special binomial, 221–224
  use of, to solve area or volume
    problems, 250
  using, at work, 254–255
quadratic formula, 238–242,
  281–282, 284
  with negative coefficients,
    244–245
  researching origin of, 256
  thinking of, as recipe, 238
  using, to solve word
    problems, 246–250

ratio, 133. *See also* slope
reciprocal, 67
rectangle, formula for area of, 284

signed numbers, 4
  addition of
    that have different
      signs, 17, 263
    that have the same
      sign, 15, 262
  multiplying and dividing, 22–24
    with different signs, 263
    with same signs, 263